THE DISCOVERY OF THE ELEMENTS

THE DISCOVER

DELACORTE PRESS / NEW Y

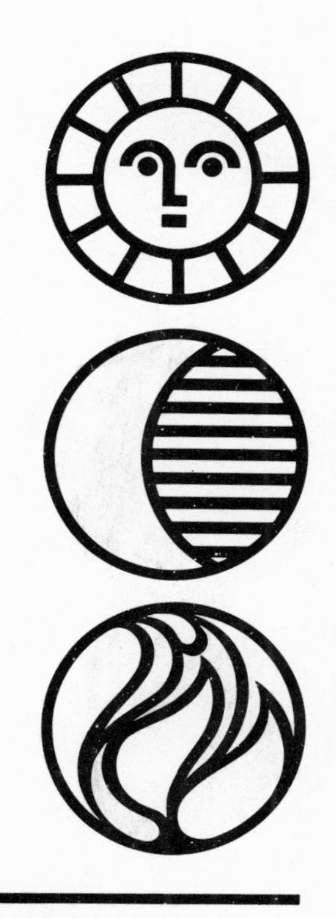

)F THE ELEMENTS

BY WILLY LEY

Library of Congress Catalog Card Number: 68–11568

DESIGNED BY *Barbara Liman*

Manufactured in the United States of America

First Printing

CONTENTS

THE DISCOVERY OF THE ELEMENTS

I. WHAT IS AN ELEMENT?

A number of years ago I overheard a remark that has stuck in my mind ever since. At a dinner party a young lady asked the man seated next to her what he did for a living. He replied, "I am a chemist," and the girl said, "I never took chemistry; it doesn't interest me." The chemist was silent; my own thought was: "If you never had a lesson in chemistry, how can you tell that it doesn't interest you? Maybe it would, if you tried."

Chemistry, it is true, has the built-in disadvantage of looking very difficult and complex. But every science, once you progress far enough, has its difficult aspects. However, the fundamentals of almost every science are easy to learn and they are usually very interesting, too.

It has become customary to call the fundamentals of a

science its "elements," for which reason there are books with titles like *Elements of Biology*, *Elements of Arithmetic*, and so forth. But the "Elements of Chemistry" would be something else—namely, the true elements, the chemical elements. They are the fundamental substances which compose everything else, the so-called building blocks of the universe.

Practically everybody, even if he never took a lesson in chemistry, can name a number of these elements. Iron is one, sulphur is another, lead still another. Oxygen and nitrogen are elements, too. But water, common rainwater, is not, though it was long thought to be an element. Water seems to have been taken to be an element simply because there is so much of it. Others thought that sand must be an element, for the same reason. Things are not that simple, however. The mere fact that a substance is abundant in Nature does not make it an element. Then how can we tell that fairly rare metals, like gold and platinum, are elements, while common substances, like water and sand, are not elements?

To arrive at the answer we have to talk about atoms first. The idea that everything consists of atoms occurred to a Greek philosopher, Demokritos, during the fifth century B.C. His reasoning is explained in Chapter VII, but at this moment we are interested in the question of what the term "atom" means when used by a chemist. It is the smallest possible particle of a substance, whether of copper, oxygen, sulphur or mercury. But while the smallest possible particle of mercury actually is one atom, the smallest single particle of oxygen consists of two atoms. It is not at all surprising that chemists failed to realize for some time that there is such a distinction. It was in 1811 that the Italian count, Amedeo Avogadro, coined the term "molecule" for the particle that consists of more than one atom. The word means "little bundle."

Keeping in mind that everything is composed of atoms, the

definition of a chemical element is simple: *It is a substance in which all atoms are of the same kind.* You may compare an element to a roll of pennies. Every one of the fifty pennies in that roll is made of the same metal and has the same shape, weight and design. But while a roll of pennies or nickels can be compared to an element, a handful of small change, consisting of pennies, nickels, dimes and quarters, is something else. Here you have four different "atoms" mixed together. Such a handful of small change would be a mixture of elements, but a mixture is not a chemical compound.

There is a simple experiment that is often performed in classrooms to explain the difference between a *mixture* of elements and a *compound* consisting of several elements. The experiment begins by mixing iron filings and pulverized sulphur as thoroughly as possible. The mixture will look like a grayish powder to the naked eye, but a good magnifying glass shows separate iron filings and grains of sulphur resting side by side. Moreover, it is possible to separate the iron filings from the sulphur grains. A magnet will attract the iron filings and leave the sulphur behind. Or else one could dump the mixed powder into water. Since both sulphur and iron are heavier than water, both will sink to the bottom of the container. But iron is about four times as heavy as sulphur. So if you shake the container, the iron will sink to the bottom faster than the sulphur. By pouring off the water before the sulphur particles have settled, most of the sulphur can be removed. Then the container is filled with clean water and shaken again. If this is done three or four times, all the sulphur will have been washed away while the iron remains behind.

Now we take another sample of the iron and sulphur mixture and heat it. For a short while nothing will happen, except that a few of the sulphur particles will burn away. But then the whole mixture will become red hot, when it has cooled, there will be a new blackish substance that has none of the characteristics of its "parent substances." It is not strong like iron but brittle and can be crushed easily. A magnet will not attract it. It will not burn. It is something new, a chemical compound of iron and sulphur. The smallest possible particle of the new substance, its molecule, still consists of sulphur and of iron atoms. But these atoms cannot be separated from each other—at least not easily—because they cling to each other. We now know that they cling together because of electrical forces; one might say that the different atoms in the molecule of a chemical compound are electrically connected.

In this example we changed a simple mixture into a compound by heating it. What are we doing if we take an ounce or so of ordinary table salt and drop it into a glass of water? After a short while no salt will be visible. Have we now made a compound of salt and water? No, all we have done is to make a *solution,* which is the same as a mixture, but a very intimate and thorough mixture. Again, it is easily possible to separate the salt from the water. All we have to do is to boil the water away and the salt will be left behind.[1]

A solution is normally liquid at room temperature, but there are solid solutions, too. If you throw iron filings into liquid glass, the iron will dissolve in the glass, incidentally coloring it green. When the glass is allowed to cool, the iron remains dissolved in it.

A mixture of two different metals (mixed when they are hot enough to be liquid) has a special name; it is called an "alloy." But it can be considered a solid solution. It does not matter whether two or three or even more different metals are mixed together; the proper term is always "alloy." There is only one exception to this rule; an alloy of a metal with

[1] A chemist would call this particular solution a "watery" (or "aqueous") solution, which does not mean that it is watery in the sense of thin; it just indicates that water has been used as the solvent. If a substance has been dissolved in alcohol, one speaks of an "alcoholic" solution.

mercury is called an "amalgam." Alloys, to repeat, are mixtures, not compounds, but separating the metals that form an alloy can be very difficult.

We now know that there are about 92 natural elements—the word "about" had to be inserted because the precise number depends on the definition of what should be considered a *natural* element, as will be discussed in a later chapter. Of these 92 elements, 11 are gases at room temperature. Another ten are nonmetallic solids, like sulphur, carbon, iodine, silicon and selenium. (Of the very rare element, astatine, it is not yet known whether it is a metal or a nonmetallic solid; most chemists suspect the latter.) All the other elements are metals.

The elements differ from each other not only in appearance and weight but also in their readiness to form compounds. Those elements which do not form compounds easily are called "inert"—the most inert of them is the gas, helium, which does not form any compounds at all. Those elements which combine easily and are, for that reason, never found in the pure state in nature, are called "active," [2] and the most active of the active elements happens also to be a gas. It is fluorine, which, for this very reason, was discovered quite late.

[2] "Active," as used here and later on in this book, means "chemically active." In books on radioactivity (explained in Chapter IX) the term "active" usually is an abbreviation for "radioactive," a distinction that must be kept in mind. A radioactive element is not necessarily chemically active.

II. THE PREHISTORIC ELEMENTS

To be known to the ancient civilizations that first arose around the Mediterranean Sea an element had to fulfill two conditions. It had to be reasonably inert, chemically speaking, so that it would stay unchanged for a long time, and it had to be present in quantities large enough to call attention to its existence.

Nine elements—not then known to be elements, of course—fulfilled these conditions. They were the metals gold, silver, copper, tin, lead and mercury, and the nonmetals carbon and sulphur. Since these elements were discovered prior to written records, they go under the designation of "prehistoric elements." They were the only elements known until about the year 1000 A.D.

Our main source for what was known about these elements

at about the time of Christ is a large work compiled by the Roman writer and Imperial Fleet Commander, Gajus Plinius Secundus. In English he is usually referred to as "Pliny the Elder" (because he had a nephew with a very similar name who is logically called "Pliny the Younger") and the book is *Natural History*. It was completed in 77 A.D. Of course, since Pliny did not know about elements in our sense, the element carbon appears in three different places, as charcoal, soot and diamond. Pliny did not even guess that these three substances were three forms of the same element. But he told about the making of charcoal, which is a fairly pure form of carbon, and one can see from his description that the way of making charcoal used by the Romans was the same as that practiced in Europe at the beginning of the present century. Soot is even purer carbon than charcoal. The Romans knew soot as the deposit that forms when a smoking oil lamp burns under something cold, like a large stone or a sheet of metal. And the Romans knew diamonds—which did not sparkle then because the art of grinding diamonds was still to be invented—but if somebody had told them that diamond is crystallized pure carbon, closely akin to soot, they would not have believed it.

But it may be more fitting to begin with gold.

Since gold is usually found in its metallic form, has a luster distinct from anything else and is also easy to shape, it is probably the oldest metal known. Somebody interested both in Biblical lore and in gold once discovered that the Bible mentions the metal 267 times, mostly because of its use for ornaments such as rings and earrings. The famous golden calf was fashioned from earrings (which were worn by both sexes) that the Israelites had brought with them from Egypt. Crowns for kings were golden, too—"and David took the crown of their king from off his head, and found it to weigh a talent of gold, and there were precious stones in it and it was set upon David's head." (1 Chronicles, XX. 2). There must be a mistake somewhere in these lines, for a talent was the equivalent of 106 pounds [1] and nobody could wear a crown that heavy, especially not in battle. What is probably meant is that the golden crown with its precious stones was worth a talent of gold.

When gold coins were still in circulation in Great Britain, the golden one-pound piece, or sovereign, bore the slang name "shiner." It is doubtful that the man who coined the term had a classical education, but it happens that his choice was apt, for the word "gold" is derived from the Sanskrit *hari,* which means both "yellow" and "shining." But it was not the color of gold that caused it to obtain "the highest rank" as Pliny expressed it. He pointed out that the color "of silver is clearer and more like the light of day, for which reason silver is preferred for our military ensigns, its brightness being visible over a greater distance."

Pliny then continued:

> Those persons are manifestly in error who think that it is its resemblance to the colors of the stars that is so prized in gold. . . . Nor yet is it for its weight or malleability that gold has been preferred to other metals, it being inferior in both these respects to lead,—but it is because gold is the only substance in nature that suffers no loss from the action of fire and passes unscathed through conflagrations and the flames of the funeral pyre.

Pliny knew that gold is often found in rivers, for example in "the Tagus in Spain, the Padus [Po] in Italy, the Hebrus in Thracia, the Pactolus in Asia and the Ganges in India." It is interesting that he failed to mention the Rhine in Germany, for *Rheingold* is not only the title of an opera (and the name

[1] A *shekel* weighed 16 grams, or 0.65 ounces; 50 shekels made one *mina,* and 60 minas one talent. Multiplying 16 times 50 times 60 gives 48,000 grams, or 105.82 pounds.

of a beer); the Rhine does carry gold and many of the old principalities proudly struck coins of Rhine gold, usually with the Latin inscription: *Sic fulgent littorae Rheni* ("So gleam the banks of the Rhine"). Apparently the Roman legions stationed along the Rhine were too preoccupied with watching the sometimes hostile Germanic tribes to notice the gold in the sand.

Pliny also knew that there were gold mines in Spain and elsewhere and he described the process of mining it at some length. But he then wrote a curious short chapter on "*auripigmentum*," a word which means "gold-colored," later shortened into the meaningless word "orpiment." *Auripigmentum* was not gold at all but a compound of sulphur and arsenic; Pliny wrote: "This substance greatly excited the hopes of the emperor Caius [Caligula], a prince most greedy for gold. He accordingly had a large quantity of it melted and really did obtain some excellent gold, but then the proportion was so extremely small that he found himself a loser thereby." The story can be explained in two ways; either some real gold happened to be mixed with this "fool's gold," or else the man in charge of the melting operation, in order to stay in the good graces of the emperor, handed over some gold with the explanation that this was all he had been able to extract from the *auripigmentum*.

Silver was the second metal known to the ancients and Pliny was well aware of the fact that gold often—he said "always"—contains a natural admixture of silver. The Greek name for such a natural gold-silver alloy was *elektron*, derived from the Greek word *elektor*, meaning "sun-glare."[2]

[2] The term *elektron* was also applied to amber in ancient Greece. And since amber was used in early experiments with electricity, the force received a name derived from that of amber. Later, when physicists needed a word for the unit of an electrical charge, the ancient Greek *elektron* was reintroduced as it stood, except for a change of the *k* to a *c* in a few languages.

The Greek *elektron* became *electrum* in Latin and Pliny claimed that *electrum* looked brighter than silver in artificial light. Because of real advantages, such as being more resistant to wear than pure gold, and fancied advantages, namely that it was said to shine with rainbow-like semicircles and made crackling noises when exposed to poison, *electrum* was often made artificially, by melting gold and silver together. The standard admixture of silver to gold seems to have been 20 to 25 percent; an alloy of these proportions still looks yellow, but gleams somewhat more brightly than pure gold.[3] Modern coin collectors know this appearance without using the name *electrum*. The gold coins of all civilized countries after about 1840 were standardized to contain 90 percent (in some cases 92 percent) of pure gold. The other 10 percent was a metal other than gold, used in order to make the alloy hard; normally this 10 percent was copper. This admixture did not change the color of the gold, which still looked as if it were pure. But in some countries the 10 percent was silver, making the coins technically *electrum*, and these do look shinier.

Silver, unless naturally alloyed with gold, is rarely found in its metallic state and its discovery must have taken place at a later date than that of gold. But we know that the Egyptians of the period of the so-called Hyksos Kings (from about 1780 B.C. to about 1580 B.C.) knew about silver, which they apparently had obtained by trading with countries in Asia. Since gold could be found much nearer to Egypt during that period, silver was considered to be twice as valuable as gold by the Egyptians.

By 1500 B.C. silver was common enough in Palestine to be used as money, though the people did not yet have coins. Most of the silver existed in the form of small bars and

[3] The "white gold" of modern jewelry is produced by adding palladium to the gold.

wedges, and payments were made and accepted on the basis of weight. The main silver-producing country of that period was Spain; the Phoenician colonizers of Spain produced it in enormous quantities. The story goes that a Greek sailor who sailed to Spain returned with silver anchors, because that was the only way in which he could carry an extra amount of the metal.

Many centuries later Pliny wrote that the best silver still came from Spain and it did come from there in large amounts; around the year 200 B.C. Cornelius Lentulus, Roman proconsul in Spain, brought 43,000 pounds of silver with him when he returned to Rome. Putting together all the scattered references in Pliny's work, one finds that the Romans used silver for everything for which we still use it: rings, chains, sandal ornaments, mirrors, silver dishes and other table ornaments, spigots and coinage. Once in a while a returning conqueror had his horse shod with silver horseshoes for a triumphant entry, something that does not seem to have been imitated often at later dates.[4]

To the Romans silver was *argentum,* an adaptation of the Greek *argyros,* which was, in turn, derived from *argos,* meaning "white." Hence, to the Greeks and Romans, silver was "the white metal"; of our word "silver" it is only known that it is of general Germanic origin (in German, *Silber*) but a specific derivation cannot be traced.

Copper is the third of the prehistoric metals and it is possible that it was used even earlier than gold. Though most of the copper now used must be extracted from its ores, metallic copper has been found on occasion in almost every country on earth. The most spectacular find of copper is probably the "lump" discovered in Minnesota in 1857, an

[4] But in 1890 the barbershop of an exclusive hotel in Chicago had a flooring made of silver dollars.

elongated piece 45 feet long, 22 feet across at its widest point and 8 feet thick in the middle; it weighed around 420 tons! To make this find even more spectacular, this particular piece of copper contained a good deal of silver, in the form of nodules large enough to be visible to the naked eye.

Primitive man was probably attracted to copper partly because of its color and partly because it could be shaped easily with a stone hammer. And it cannot have been very long until artisans discovered that their hammering hardened the copper. The oldest copper utensils we know come from Egypt and are believed to have been made in about 4000 B.C. Sumerian copper utensils also date from before 3000 B.C.

By the time of Pliny pure copper, which even after work hardening is still quite soft, had given way to a substance Pliny called *aes*, a much mistranslated word. For centuries, to the confusion of everybody, *aes* was translated as "brass" by English-speaking writers. Since the alloy was a copper-tin alloy, it should have been called "bronze," for brass is a copper-zinc alloy and zinc was not recognized as a separate metal until about 1,500 years later. Copper-tin alloys seem to have been fashioned first by the Chinese. When the Western world first became acquainted with bronze, the Phoenicians, always possessed of a superb business sense, started looking for tin, probably finding mines first in what is now Portugal. Then they somehow learned that the metal needed to improve copper existed on islands which to them were far to the north. The actual place was Cornwall, England, but the trading center was the Isle of Wight (then named "*Iktis*"), where the Phoenicians loaded their ships. Possibly there was also an overland trading route for tin along the Elbe River.

Probably because tin, like lead, has a low melting point, the Romans first considered it a variety of lead and spoke of *plumbum album* (white lead) when they meant tin, and *plumbum nigrum* (black lead) when they meant lead. After Pliny, the word *stannum* for tin became customary.[5]

But we are not completely done with copper yet. A persistent story claims that some of the ancient artisans knew the secret of making "hard copper" without alloying it. The "secret" consisted of smelting a copper ore that was naturally contaminated with something unknown that caused the metal to be hard. Early copper implements from Hungary are now known to contain between 3 and 4.5 percent of antimony, some copper utensils from Egypt contain 3 to 4 percent arsenic and some from Germany 3 to 4 percent nickel; they all were natural bronzes but not so good as true bronze, the copper-tin alloy.

Of course, copper was also a coinage metal almost everywhere and the copper coins of the Roman Empire were quite pure. In 1965 fourteen Roman copper coins from the period from 21 B.C. to 54 A.D. were carefully analyzed and it was found that the copper content (with two exceptions) was always above 99 percent; the average works out to about 99.3 percent. The two exceptions were of brass in our sense, one containing 18.1 percent zinc, the other 12 percent zinc. The latter had been minted in Lugdunum (modern Lyons, France); the others had been minted in Rome.

Lead, the next of the prehistoric metals, was also known in very early times. A leaden idol, dated about 2200 B.C., has been found at Troy. Both the Israelites and the Egyptians used sheets of lead as durable writing materials; fishermen weighted their nets with lead, and in Roman times lead was used for water pipes. Some Roman water pipes found at

[5] The English "tin" and the German "*Zinn*" (pronounced "tsinn") are both derived from the Old High German word *zin,* meaning "little stick," the form in which the metal probably was traded.

Bath, England, had a wall thickness of half an inch and an internal diameter of four to five inches. Because lead was so cheap and so easy to work, the Romans used it not only for water tanks and piping but also for cooking and drinking utensils. It now seems that most Romans (except the very rich in whose households the eating utensils were made of silver) suffered from a mild case of lead poisoning all their lives. It is quite possible that the short average life-span of the Romans can be blamed on the continuous use of lead in daily living; the symptoms of lead poisoning were probably thought to be simply the natural signs of aging.

> We must [next] give an account of the metal known as iron, at the same time the most useful and the most fatal instrument in the hands of mankind. For by the aid of iron we lay open the ground, we plant [fruit] trees, we prepare our vineyard trees and we force our vines each year to resume their youthful state, by cutting away their decayed branches. It is by the aid of iron that we construct houses, cleave rocks and perform so many other useful offices of life. But it is with iron also that wars, murders and robberies are effected and this not only hand to hand, but from a distance even.

This was, of course, Pliny speaking, somehow ignoring the fact that bronze had done all these jobs, good and bad, before iron was introduced. While it is both customary and convenient to divide the early history of humanity into the Stone Age, the Bronze Age and the Iron Age, there must have been a number of iron implements and weapons around at any time, even during the latter portion of the Stone Age. For iron can be found in its pure state—and in the more useful state of an iron-nickel alloy—because of meteorite falls. There are now an estimated 450 tons of meteoric iron in museums and private collections. It must be assumed that early man, when he learned that this material could be made useful, had a similar supply available. And meteorite impacts are completely random; the material that was to become a great hero's sword could fall from heaven at any time or any place.

The supply of meteoric iron, however, is uncertain and there is rarely enough of it to serve as the basis of even a modest industry. The Iron Age, based on terrestrial iron, began about the year 1400 B.C. in the eastern Mediterranean and around 500 B.C. in western Europe. By the time of Christ, as can be inferred from Pliny, it was common in Rome but it must still have been fairly expensive for a few centuries to come because it was specifically stated that all the men in Charlemagne's army were armed with iron.

The last of the metals known in antiquity and also the last to be discovered was mercury. The mercury mines of Almadén in Spain seem to have been started about 400 B.C. and the first mention of the metal can be found in the writings of Aristotle (384–322 B.C.) It is not mentioned in the *Odyssey* of Homer (around 800 B.C.), which makes it pretty certain that it was unknown then, at least to the Greeks.

The Greek name for mercury was *hydrargyros,* a combination of the Greek words for water (*hydor*) and silver (*argyros*), while the Romans called it *argentum vivum* or "living silver." Unlike lead, the poisonous characteristics of mercury were recognized early and warnings are abundant whenever mercury is mentioned. But mercury is a fascinating metal, and, although the Arab physicians of a later period knew about its poisonous qualities just as their Greek and Roman predecessors had, rich Arabs of the ninth and tenth centuries had pools of mercury installed in their pleasure gardens in Córdoba, Cairo and Baghdad.

The astrologers of the third and second centuries B.C. must have been most pleased by the existence of mercury. They had their "seven planets"—the sun, moon, Mercury,

Venus, Mars, Jupiter and Saturn—and they had acquired the habit of "assigning" different metals to each of the planets. Gold, of course, was the metal of the sun, silver, that of the moon, iron, that of warlike Mars and so forth (Figure 1). Without the quicksilver of Spain there would have been no metal to go with fast-moving Mercury.

Sulphur is the second nonmetallic element known to the ancients. Since its occurrence is usually associated with volcanoes, it can be found in many places in the volcanic Med-

SUN	○	Gold
MOON	☾	Silver
MERCURY	☿	Quicksilver
VENUS	♀	Copper
MARS	♂	Iron
JUPITER	♃	Tin
SATURN	♄	Lead

FIGURE 1. *The symbols for the "seven planets" and the "seven metals."*

iterranean region. What seems to have impressed the ancients most was the fact that sulphur can be ignited so easily; the words "sulphur" and "fire" were often used interchangeably. In the Bible, the word that is rendered as "brimstone" in the English translation sometimes actually means "sulphur," but more frequently it means "fire" or the "essence of fire."

To the Greeks sulphur had a decidedly religious connotation, presumably because sulphur could be found near hot springs, which were considered sacred and of supernatural origin. Even the Greek name for sulphur, *theion,* is traceable to older words that mean "sacrifice" and sulphur was used in sacrifices and other religious ceremonies.

But the religious aspects did not prevent the ancients from making very practical use of the substance, too. In the Homeric legend, Odysseus, after he had killed his wife's suitors, ordered the slaves to burn sulphur in the great hall for the purpose of cleansing it. The bleaching properties of sulphur were known also; cloth that was to be bleached was hung under a structure resembling a large bell in which sulphur was burned. Roman wine merchants used it to fumigate their cellars. From all these uses it was very well known that the fumes of burning sulphur were irritating and could not be endured when concentrated. For this reason sulphur was used during military sieges, if the wind was right. The earliest known case of such a gas attack was a siege of a Greek city that took place in 424 B.C.

III. THE ALCHEMISTS AND THE ELEMENTS

While a well-read Roman of Pliny's time would know most of what was then known about nine actual elements, he would have believed that there were only four elements. Believing this, he would have followed the reasoning of the Greek philosophers who had derived their opinions from speculations about the beginning of the world.

They considered it logical that the world had begun with unshaped matter and it followed that all the matter that was to form the world would be of just one kind. Up to that point most philosophers were in agreement, but when it came to the question of what the "original matter" had been, they differed sharply. Thales of Miletos, around the year 600 B.C., was convinced that everything had started with water. Anaximenes, about a century later, was equally convinced that air was the original matter, and Heraclitus, another century later, was certain that everything had started with fire. But he was careful to point out that he did not mean ordinary fire such as a shepherd might use to cook his meal, but that the original fire had been a kind of divine and supernatural fire.

It was Empedocles, in 450 B.C., who compromised by suggesting that the original matter might have been of several kinds. He proposed four "original elements," namely, earth, water, air and fire. From the point of view of a modern chemist it was the worst possible choice: for earth is a mixture of all the true elements, water is a compound of two elements, air is merely a mixture of two elements and fire is not a substance at all but a process, the process of oxidation.

Aristotle, the all-around genius of the ancient world, accepted the scheme of Empedocles and enlarged upon it. Earth, he said, was "naturally" dry and cold. Fire, of course, was dry and hot. Water was cold and wet while air could be hot or cold. Aristotle's reasoning can be shown nicely in a diagram (Figure 2). Everything that existed, he said, consisted of these four elements and their attributes (hot or cold, wet or dry) in different proportions. Aristotle's ideas would not have been a helpful guide for actual chemical work, but as something that could be learned and taught, they worked fine. Philosophers were satisfied with them for the next 1,800 years.

But slowly there came into being a group of people who were not satisfied with just four elements and four attributes. These people eventually came to be called "alchemists." Their basic reasoning was that, if Nature had changed the "first matter" into an endless variety of substances, one should be able to duplicate this in the laboratory. And if Nature had changed some of the "first matter" into dull lead, and some of it into gleaming gold, one should be able to

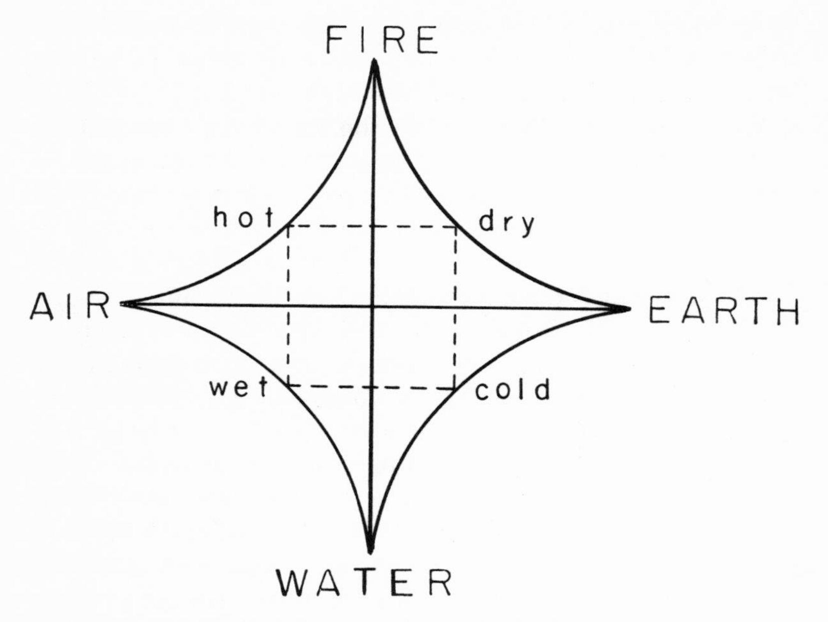

FIGURE 2. *Modern representation of the classical "four elements" and their characteristics.*

change lead into gold, a change that was called "transmutation."

Alchemists, as a group, were very puzzling to later historians. Some historians put it bluntly and said they were people who tried to make gold. Others said that they were charlatans who swindled people out of money with the promise of making gold. Still others pointed out that alchemists were magicians, or at least thought they were. And a few historians came to the conclusion that the alchemists should be considered the forerunners of chemists. It so happens that every one of these statements is true. There were alchemists who merely tried to make gold in order to be rich. There were others who were out and out mountebanks. And there were some who experimented in order to understand nature, though with hopes for gold somewhere along the line.

For the purpose of this book it is simplest to say that alchemists tried to make gold. And if this definition is used, it seems that the first alchemists can be found among the Arabs.

During the seventh century the Arabs established a large but loosely organized empire along the North African coast, then moved into Spain. The Arabs were eager to conquer new lands, but they did not come as destroyers. They merely intended to be the new rulers. Their learning, for which they had great zest, began with the reading of the works of non-Arabic scholars. Then, for their own convenience, they translated these works into Arabic; so through them we know of a number of classical works of which the originals are lost, but the Arabic translations were preserved. However, they did not just translate; they also wrote many books of their own, at first mainly about medicine and geography. But among the Arabic writings there are books specifically devoted to alchemy, to the art of the transmutation of metals, in short, to making gold.

The most famous Arab alchemist was one Abu Musa Jabir, who is said to have lived from about 721 to about 815, and is reported to have been a personal friend of the vizier of the famous caliph Harun-al-Rashid. When some of his books appeared in Latin translation at a later date, the name was spelled "Geber." As time went on more and more original manuscripts by "Geber" were found and by about 1800 a number of historians had become thoroughly suspicious. There could be no doubt that the manuscripts that had been "found" had been written at a later date. If they were not genuine, how about the early ones? Some scientists were content with splitting the "Geber" manuscripts into two groups, one actually written by a historical Geber (or Jabir) around the year 800, the other written by later alchemists and adorned with the great name so that they might be more readily accepted. But another school of thought asked what documentation could be shown to prove that there actually had been a Geber.

In short, we do not know whether there was such a man. But since later alchemists accepted the works as genuine, we might as well continue to speak of "Geber"; even if he did not exist, the works under that name had much influence. They were written in an obtuse style, shrouded in mysticism, often using symbolical language that can hardly be deciphered now. The enemies of alchemy (there were some at all times) made fun of Geber's style. What Geber does seem to have said is that there are only two elements: sulphur, or the principle of combustion, and mercury, the principle of being metallic.

All Arabs did not agree with alchemical theory; the majority, in fact, was sharply critical. But alchemy spread to other countries; after all, even if "Geber" was completely wrong, there was nothing in any philosophy that said that one metal could *not* be changed into another metal. Most of the active alchemists thought that the road to success consisted of hard work. And they worked. Of course, they also prayed for success, some of them because they believed in prayer, others because they did not wish to be accused of having resorted to black magic.

Some, like the famous Raimundus Lullus (*c.*1235–1315) of Spain took the position that alchemy was a "talent" that could not be learned and could not be taught. But this position did not prevent Lull from giving long and complicated recipes, since it was expected of him.

An alchemist, when asked what he wanted to accomplish, might truthfully say that he wanted to make gold and thereby grow rich. Or he might say that he hoped to find the *aurum potabile,* the "drinkable gold," which would surely cure any illness. Or he might say, as some did, that the *aurum potabile,* being a boon to mankind, was preferable but that the making of solid gold was useful, too, since at least it cured "the great illness of poverty." But the ambitious alchemist hoped for the substance the Arabs had called "*al-iksīr*" (the ancestor of the word "elixir") which was later named the "philosopher's stone." In appearance it was said to be a red powder and one part of this powder was supposed to be capable of changing a thousand parts of mercury or of lead into gold. Applied to gold, *al-iksīr* would convert it into drinkable gold to cure sickness.

The technical term for an alchemist who had succeeded was "adept," but the fact is that many people who called themselves adepts were simply hanged by outraged kings and dukes who had financed their labors for years.

Now what did a sincere alchemist believe?

His beliefs were based on a few facts and a principle which was expressed in Latin: *Corpora non agunt nisi fluida,* which means in English, "Bodies do not act unless they [or at least one of them] are liquid." The facts were that mercury was a metal but it was liquid; mercury and sulphur formed a red substance, namely cinnabar, so they could be combined, even showing the red color of the mysterious *al-iksīr.* The next question to be asked was: Why was mercury liquid? Obviously there was a special force that kept mercury from congealing and this force was called a "basilisk." Now, in order to make mercury solid, thus turning it into silver, some way of driving out the basilisk had to be found. But the basilisk had to go somewhere, so a new home had to be provided for it. But the goal was gold and gold differed from silver mainly by being yellow. Logically, then, there should be a substance that colored the mercury yellow at the moment it turned solid. Yellow sulphur seemed to be the proper substance for this.

Hence sulphur and mercury had to go into the mixture, plus something liquid (remember a liquid had to be present and the mercury was supposed to turn solid) and something that was a new home for the basilisk that had been driven from the quicksilver. The problem was to find the right substances.

This is a much condensed version of alchemical reasoning. In an alchemical book this explanation would have taken one or two long chapters or maybe the whole book because several authorities would have been cited for each statement, opposing authorities would have been refuted, appropriate prayers would have been suggested at intervals, and, of course, the various ingredients would not simply have been named. They would either have appeared as symbols (Figure 3) or else would have been encoded in words, like "the pale yellow offspring of the red ore of Iberia," meaning sulphur derived from cinnabar. And the names of Aristotle and Geber (especially Geber) would have been used liberally.

Thousands of alchemists worked many thousands of man-years to accomplish the task, never completely despairing, but never successful. With all this work, one would imagine that they at least advanced chemistry, for example by discovering some elements.

The answer is very nearly "no." All this work did not even produce new chemical methods or instruments. The alchemists merely copied what Arab chemists and artisans had used centuries earlier. Concluding around 1760, the whole alchemical period yielded just eight new elements. Only one of them, phosphorus, can be said to have been found by an alchemist; the others were discoveries of miners, smelters and apothecaries. The other seven elements were all metals,

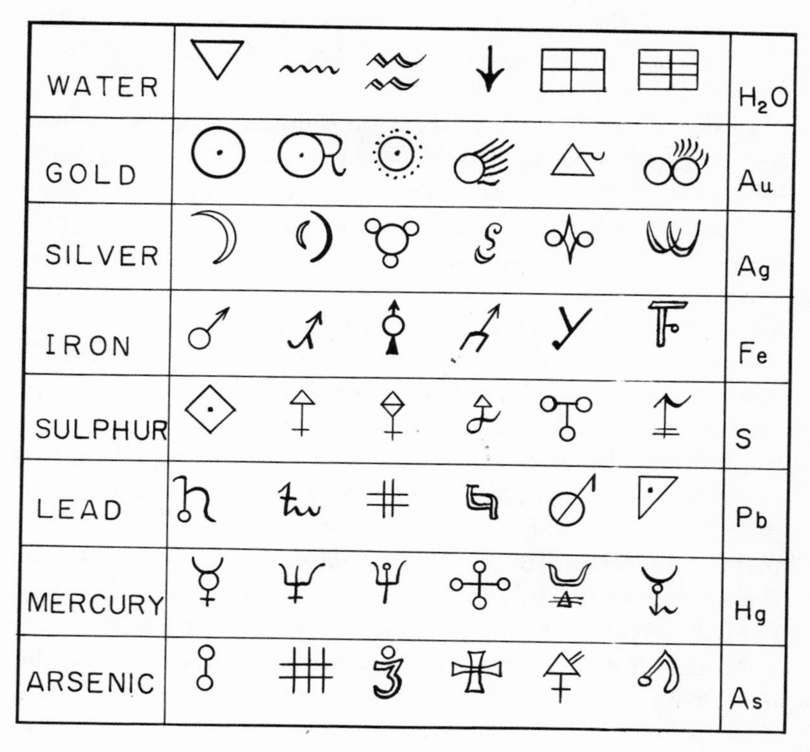

FIGURE 3. *Symbols used by the alchemists.*

namely arsenic, antimony, cobalt, nickel, platinum, zinc and bismuth.

Of these, arsenic and antimony were the first two to be added to the list of known elements but there is no sure way of telling when and by whom. Both of them are metals and, though this fact must have been noticed at an early date, there was a curious reluctance to call them metals. The alchemists had taken over the notion of seven metals from antiquity and, since there were seven metals, there could not be nine. Besides, what planets were to "rule" arsenic and antimony if they were metals? Therefore, they were called "bastard metals" by some, while others just took them to be varieties of lead.

In doing so, the alchemists were following the example of the classical authors, for these two metals were actually known in antiquity but were not recognized as separate metals. The compound of antimony and sulphur is a pronounced black in color and it was used to darken the eyebrows of women and to improve the appearance of the dead and even of statues of gods. The Egyptians called it *"stimmi,"* the Arabs later called it *"kuhul,"* meaning "fine powder"; when equipped with the Arabic article *al,* this gave the word *"al-kuhul,"* from which we derive our "alcohol." That antimony was also known in its metallic form is proved by two facts. We have a vase of Chaldean origin which is made of practically pure antimony, with only a trace of iron in the metal. The other fact is in Pliny's work where he wrote that the heating of the substance that was to produce *stimmi* had to be done very carefully, "or else it will turn into lead."

Around the year 1610 there appeared the first book on the new metal, with the title *The Triumphal Chariot of Antimony* by Basilius Valentinus. It was published by Johann Thölde of Hesse, a city councilor of the small town of Frankenhausen in Thuringia, who was also the overseer and manager of a small salt mine in the area. Johann Thölde claimed to have translated the book from a Latin manuscript of a monk, Brother Basilius Valentinus, who was then regarded as the discoverer of antimony. But then the whole case turned out to be a repetition of what probably happened in the case of Geber. Many experts were agreed that Thölde had written the book himself and that "Basilius Valentinus" was a figment of his imagination. But one German by the name of Gudenus claimed in 1675 that a monk of that name had actually lived in 1413 at the St. Peter Monastery near Erfurt, but there is no evidence that he wrote anything. It would seem, therefore, that Thölde was the author of the book but used the name of a man who had died about 150 years earlier and of whom he had heard.

The first serious work on the chemistry of antimony was written by Nicolas Lemery (1645–1715), a French apothecary.

The history of arsenic is a little clearer than that of antimony. What the Romans called arsenic was not the metal itself, but its compound with sulphur, mainly the "orpiment" which Emperor Caligula had burned in the hopes of obtaining gold. The honor of having produced the metal arsenic is usually accorded to the German scholar and churchman, Albertus Magnus (1193–1280), who wrote that it could be obtained by heating orpiment with soap, two parts of soap for every part of orpiment. There was still some confusion in the minds of alchemists because one of the sulphur compounds of arsenic looks very much like cinnabar, the sulphur compound of mercury. Since they insisted in clinging to their "seven metals," arsenic was labeled a variety of mercury.

In the sixteenth century metallic arsenic was obtained once more, by an unruly character who was a physician but dabbled in alchemy, chemistry, mysticism and even astronomy—Paracelsus.[1] Paracelsus heated orpiment with eggshells. But this was an isolated case; since Paracelsus was forever engaged in violent disputations with practically everybody, his opinions were discounted most of the time.

Arsenic entered the scientific phase of its career in 1649 when the German apothecary, Johann Schroeder, published a so-called pharmacopoeia (a book of medical remedies) in

[1] His full name was Philippus Aureolus Paracelsus, while his original name was Theophrastus Bombastus von Hohenheim—the last name means "from the heights" and his classical pseudonym, "Paracelsus," has the same meaning.

which he gave clear directions for obtaining metallic arsenic. If the arsenic compound was orpiment, that is, the sulphur compound or sulphide, it was to be heated with lime; if the arsenic compound was the oxide of arsenic, it was to be heated with charcoal. Early in the eighteenth century several researchers, namely Johann Friedrich Henckel (in 1725), Georg Brandt (in 1733) and John Brownall (in 1744), wrote treatises on the chemistry of arsenic and Brownall pointed out that arsenic, like sulphur, is present in small amounts in most ores.

The next element to be discovered was phosphorus, in 1669. The discoverer was a Hamburg merchant named Hennig Brandt, not related to the Georg Brandt who has just been mentioned in connection with arsenic. As a young man, Hennig Brandt was a soldier; later he became a physician whose skill was doubted by all other physicians and by most of his patients. Still, he married a wealthy girl and, discovering how comfortable it was to have money, he tried to make more. He became an alchemist and began to reason in a manner that was weird even for an alchemist. Since gold is the only yellow metal, and all the experiments with yellow sulphur had led nowhere, Brandt looked for other things that were yellow. Yellow flowers he considered unsuitable, but human urine sometimes looked yellow and so he embarked on a series of experiments with urine, which at least had the advantage of not costing any money.

Just how he went about his experiments is not known for he kept the procedure secret. He probably let the urine evaporate first to reduce its bulk, then permitted it to ferment and finally distilled the resulting liquid. What he obtained was a waxy substance that could be melted easily, but usually burst into flames in the process. The most impressive aspect was that it glowed in the dark. The news about the substance spread quickly, although the secret of preparing it was kept for a while. Brandt had been criticized by other physicians for "not knowing a single word of Latin," which must have been true, for any other learned man would have thought of a classical name for the new substance, but Brandt called it "*kaltes Feuer*" (cold fire) and sometimes "my fire."

In the history of science, many discoveries and inventions have been made almost simultaneously by people working entirely independently of each other. The discovery of phosphorus was no exception. Hennig Brandt had a famous contemporary, Johann Kunckel von Löwenstern (1630–1702). He was the son of an alchemist and as a young man had studied pharmacy, assaying ores and the making of glass. That he was an outstanding man is shown by the list of his employers; he worked in the laboratory of Johann Georg II, the Elector of Saxony [2] at Dresden, then near Berlin as manager of the glass works of Friedrich Wilhelm, the Elector of Brandenburg. While there, Kunckel invented ruby glass and his grateful sovereign gave him an island in a lake near Berlin, the *Pfaueninsel* (peacock island), as a present, "with the privileges of baking his own bread and brewing his own beer." [3] Finally Kunckel served King Charles XI of Sweden, who made him Baron von Löwenstern.

One day when he was in Hamburg, Kunckel showed a friend a phosphorescent substance that he had made (we don't know just what it was). The friend told him that a local resident, Hennig Brandt, had a much more remarkable substance. So Kunckel called on Brandt. Brandt, as it happened, was all out of phosphorus but took Kunckel to the house of a friend to whom he had given some.

Kunckel immediately wrote to a friend of his, Dr. Johann

[2] Seven German princes bore the title of Elector because their duty was to elect a German emperor in case the normal line of succession should be broken.

[3] The privilege consisted in not having to join the Brewer's Guild in case he wished to brew beer.

Daniel Krafft in Dresden. Krafft went to Hamburg without delay to buy the secret from Hennig Brandt for 200 thalers. Kunckel, who apparently was after the secret himself, happened to arrive at Brandt's house while Krafft was there and, in the violent argument that followed, Brandt or Krafft let it slip that the raw material was urine. That was enough for Kunckel; he knew all the chemical tricks of his time. Half a year later he could make phosphorus himself and he gave it its name, from Greek *phos,* meaning "light," and *phero,* "I bear." Kunckel also kept the process secret because he feared that the new and unreliable substance might cause conflagrations in the hands of careless or unskilled people. Duke Johann Friedrich of Hanover was so impressed that he ordered a yearly pension to be paid to Kunckel for the rest of his life.

But discoveries are not only made in duplicate but occasionally even in triplicate. The English chemist, Robert Boyle (1627–1691), also discovered phosphorus and his assistant, Ambrose Godfrey Hackwitz, who dealt in pharmacological supplies, started making it for sale, at the price of three pounds sterling per ounce, again without revealing the process. In 1737 an unnamed stranger appeared in Paris, offering the secret for sale to the Academy of Sciences. The Academy paid the price and appointed Jean Hellot to test whether one could actually make phosphorus in the manner the man described. When Hellot reported that it could be done, the Academy published his report, and the secret ceased to be one.

In 1670 the Swedish chemist, Carl Wilhelm Scheele, discovered that it was easier to extract phosphorus from bones and published his method. But so far nobody knew what phosphorus really was. It was the French chemist, Antoine Laurent Lavoisier (1743–1794), who proved it to be an element.

Compared with the turbulent story of phosphorus, the stories of the discoveries of the other elements found during that period are tame and undramatic. Though cobalt and nickel were discovered by two different people in two different years, their stories belong together. For many years honest miners had been annoyed by the fact that, on occasion, honest copper ores, smelted according to honest tradition, simply failed to produce copper. The miners may have been honest, but they were also superstitious and they felt sure that a mischievous something had operated to deprive them of the results of their toil. Their idea was somewhat like the alchemist's belief in a basilisk in mercury, but since they were not learned men, they did not use classical terms. They said that a *Kobold* (mountain gnome) or a *Nickel* (river gnome) had "possessed" the copper.

The discoverer of cobalt was Georg Brandt (1694–1768), who was born at Riddarhytta, Sweden, as the son of an apothecary who later in his life operated a copper smelter. Young Brandt studied in The Netherlands and obtained a medical doctorate in France, but he never practiced medicine. After his return to his native country, Brandt was first placed in charge of the laboratory of the Royal School of Mines, was then transferred to the Royal Mint, and in 1730 became assay master of the mint. After an investigation of arsenic and its compounds, Brandt became interested in a mysterious mineral. Acid solutions of this mineral looked blue as did the solutions of copper ores. But this mineral, when dissolved in liquid glass, also colored the glass blue, something copper ores did not do. European glassmakers used it when they wanted blue glass, and we now know that the Egyptians used the same mineral for the same purpose, except that they claimed that their blue glass beads were blue gems.

In 1735 Brandt succeeded in separating the metal from its

ore and named it "cobalt." Interestingly enough, he also referred to it as a "half-metal." But in his case it was not a holdover of alchemical ideas; in fact, Brandt spent many years of his later life in writing treatise after treatise against the follies of alchemy. He just used a different criterion. The ancient metals were all malleable; they could be formed by hammering. Cobalt happens to be brittle and for this reason Brandt considered it metal-like, but not properly a metal.

The other ore that should have yielded copper in the opinion of the miners was a heavy brownish ore, now called "niccolite." Glassmakers used it to color glass green, but the miners despised it. It was, of course, nickel ore, and the man who first isolated it was another Swede, Baron Axel Fredrik Cronstedt (1722–1765). His father had been a lieutenant general in the Swedish army, which fact enabled the son to obtain the best education then available, studying mathematics and the physical sciences.

Experimenting with the ore, Cronstedt also looked for copper at first. Then he scraped off the greenish crystals that had formed on a lump of the ore and heated them with charcoal, obtaining—to his surprise, no doubt—a silvery metal. After studying its properties, he published a report in the *Memoirs of the Stockholm Academy,* announcing it as a new metal and proposing the name of "nickel."

A French chemist, Balthasar-Georges Sage (1740–1824) doubted that Cronstedt had obtained a new metal in 1754 and said that the nickel of Cronstedt was probably just a mixture of cobalt, arsenic, iron and copper. That statement appeared in a French chemical journal in 1773, after Cronstedt had died. Two years later it prompted another Swedish chemist, Torbern Bergman (1735–1784) to repeat the experiment. He found that iron, arsenic and cobalt were indeed present, but only as impurities. By refining the nickel, he was able to defend Cronstedt's results and after that the existence of the new metal was no longer doubted.

Half a century later the masters of the mints of various countries began to try to use nickel for coins. Early experiments proved disastrous. Nickel was so tough that normal pressure in the coining machines produced such a shallow impression that a freshly minted piece looked as if it had been going from hand to hand for at least a dozen years. The logical thing to do was to increase the pressure, but then the dies wore out, or actually broke, very soon.

Small additions of silver or copper, around 15 percent, did not help and it was not until after it had been learned that the nickel should be an addition to copper (in our coins, 25 percent) that "nickel" coins could be minted successfully.

Just about the time when Axel Cronstedt began to tackle the heavy brown ore that yielded nickel, news of another unknown metal began to arrive from the New World. In 1741 an English metallurgist by the name of Charles Wood found in South America some of the silvery metal that is now called "platinum," the most valuable of all commercial metals. Wood sent a few samples of the metal to a relative in England. The relative, Dr. William Brownrigg, performed a number of tests and, after several years, in December 1750, turned the specimens over to the Royal Society of London, calling the metal by its Spanish name, *platina de pinto.*

Meanwhile more information about the new metal had become available from another source. A Spanish naval officer, Don Antonio de Ulloa (1716–1795), had been sent to Peru in 1735 by King Philip V of Spain. Don Antonio de Ulloa was a mathematician and a good all-around scientist. On his return in 1744 he was briefly arrested by the British because he traveled on a French ship while Great Britain and France were at war. But he was permitted to return home with all his specimens and notebooks (in fact, during his short stay in England he was elected a member of the Royal Society) and the log of the voyage was published in 1748. It contained the surprising information that the Spaniards in Peru had mined the silvery metal and had used it to "stretch" their supply of gold used for coinage. Since the government could not permit their good gold coins to be "adulterated" in this manner, the platinum mines were closed and the metal already mined was ordered to be thrown into the sea!

While the specimens sent to Europe by Charles Wood are the first samples known to have reached Europe, they were probably preceded by others. In 1557 the Italian scholar and poet, Julius Caesar Scaliger, wrote that a then current definition of a metal, "a substance that can be melted and hardens again on cooling" would leave out two metals, namely mercury that does not harden (it just doesn't get cold enough in Italy) and a new metal from Mexico "which no fire . . . has yet been able to liquefy."

We now know that the melting point of gold is 1,063° centigrade while that of platinum is 1,755° centigrade so that a furnace that can melt gold would leave platinum untouched. And while there are a few other metals with melting points even higher than that of platinum,[4] none of them was known, or likely to be known, at the time. Scaliger's remark, therefore, can refer only to platinum, which probably did not even have a distinctive name yet.

At first, nobody had much use for platinum because it was too difficult to work. About 1798 Dr. William Hyde Wollas-

[4] They are: titanium (1,800°), thorium (1,845°), uranimum (1,850°), niobium, formerly called "columbium" (1,950°), rhodium (1,955°), iridium (2,350°), ruthenium (2,450°), osmium (2,700°), molybdenum (2,820°), tantalum (2,850°), rhenium (3,000°) and, at the top of the list, wolfram, formerly called "tungsten" (3,370°). All melting points are given in degrees centigrade.

ton discovered a method of working it and he acquired a fortune of nearly 30,000 pounds sterling as a result of his discovery so that, at the age of thirty-four, he retired in 1800 in order to devote all his time to scientific work. Still, even though platinum could now be worked, nobody needed it except chemists, who used it for high-temperature crucibles. The English continued to call it "frog's gold" and, as late as 1874, the price was just about one pound sterling per ounce.

In the meantime the Russians had discovered platinum in considerable quantities in the northern part of the Ural mountains. The year was 1820, and the Department of Mines of the Russian government paid the finder the sum of six dollars for an amount of platinum weighing about two pounds. The Russian government could not think of any use for the metal either and called on two famous foreign scientists to help. One was the Swedish chemist, Baron Jöns Jacob Berzelius (1779–1848), the other the German naturalist, Baron Alexander von Humboldt (1769–1859). Berzelius received half a pound of so-called platinum sands with the request for a chemical investigation. Alexander von Humboldt was invited to inspect the sites personally and to suggest a use for platinum. He either suggested that coins might be made of the metal, or else he approved the suggestion if it had been made by somebody else. The first factory for refining platinum was built at St. Petersburg, then the capital of Russia. The Russian government began issuing three-ruble pieces in 1828, six-ruble pieces in 1829 and 12-ruble pieces in 1830. Four and a half million coins were struck, until 1845. This, incidentally, was the only time coins were ever made of the metal.

Interestingly, the Russian government was ashamed of these coins and they were not permitted to leave Russia. Nobody objected if travelers took Russian gold and silver coins with them, but the platinum coins, if they had any, had to be exchanged for gold at the border. Russia did not wish to appear poor in the eyes of the world!

At present, the price of platinum is several times that of the same weight of gold. Originally platinum was found in the form of nuggets or dust, like gold, but it also occurs as an "impurity" in nickel ores and the larger part of the platinum now produced is a by-product of the refining of nickel.

The metal zinc resembles tin to a certain extent and its melting point (420°) is not too different from that of lead (328°) so that its presence in metal from mixed ores was not easily noticed. Because of this it is impossible to ascertain the exact year when the element zinc was discovered.

Moreover, the metal was used in Asia at an earlier date than in Europe, but specific dates cannot be established, except in one case. One of the Indian kings, Madanapala by name, wrote a medical dictionary in which zinc is mentioned as one of the metals, under the name of "*jasada.*" We don't know precisely when this dictionary was written, but the date must have been near 1374.

It was known in classical times that copper alloyed with zinc to make bronze occasionally turned a lighter and almost golden color. The Greek physician and writer, Dioscorides, who lived during the first century A.D., said such additions were deliberately made in his time. If *kadmeia* is added to the copper, he wrote, it will look much better—that can only refer to zinc ore. Strangely enough, German miners of the late Middle Ages and afterwards adopted this Greek word, turning it into *Galmei* (pronounced "gal-My") for zinc ore while their name for the metal was *zinken.*

The latter word appears for the first time in the *Chronicle of the Country Carynthia* by Paracelsus, written in 1538. He said there that in that area one can find "Zinken, which is not found elsewhere in Europe, a most strange metal . . .

can be melted but is not malleable." The German, Andreas Libavius (1550?–1616), who was a physician and teacher, called zinc "the eighth metal," something Paracelsus had avoided doing.

Still another name for zinc that was used during the sixteenth century was *Conterfait* or *Conterfey* because zinc, with copper, produces a counterfeit of gold. The master smelter, Löhneys, who worked at Goslar, wrote in 1617: "When the metals form a melt, a metal accumulates at the bottom in the spaces between the bricks which the masters call Zink or Conterfey. By knocking a hole in the front wall the metal has a way out and runs into a trough provided for it. This metal is white like tin but harder and more brittle, it sounds like a little bell."

The year 1746 is the year of the scientific discovery of zinc. The chemist, Andreas Sigismund Marggraf (1709–1782) heated a mixture of calamine [5] and charcoal in a closed vessel, without the presence of copper that had always been thought necessary, and obtained a metal that differed from all known metals in specific gravity, melting point and chemical characteristics.

The last of the metals discovered during this period was bismuth and the first to recognize it as a metal in its own right was a man who called himself Georgius Agricola (1494–1555). His real name was Bauer, but since this is the German word for peasant, it is easy to understand why Bauer used the Latin equivalent of this word; a doctor named "peasant" is not likely to inspire much confidence. Born in Saxony, he first studied theology and classical languages and actually taught Greek for some time at the City School of Zwickau. Then he went to Italy and returned home with a

[5] A further evolution of the word *galmei*.

medical doctorate. Since he lived in a mining area, most of his patients were miners, from whom he apparently learned a great deal about metals. Agricola wrote several books about minerals and mining. His main work, *De re metallica* (On Metals), was first printed one year after its author's death and has been called "the greatest treatise of technological chemistry, mining, geology and engineering of early modern times." For centuries it existed only in its Latin original version and in Italian and German translations, but in 1912 Herbert Clark Hoover, later president of the United States, translated it into English with the assistance of his wife.

Agricola wrote:

> Bismuth ore, free from every kind of silver, is smelted by various methods. First a small pit is dug in the dry ground; into this pulverized charcoal is thrown and tamped in, and then it is dried with burning charcoal. Afterward, thick dry pieces of beechwood are placed over the pit, and the bismuth ore is thrown on it. As soon as the kindled wood burns, the heated ore drips with bismuth, which runs down into the pit from which, when cooled the cakes are removed. Because pieces of burnt wood, or often charcoal and occasionally slag, drop into the bismuth which collects in the pit, and make it impure, it is put back into another kind of crucible to be melted so that pure cakes may be made.[6]

Agricola, as this excerpt shows, treated bismuth as something well known to miners and not as a recent discovery. Older sources have been found, one of which is a mention of *Wysmud* by the burgomaster, Ruelein von Kalbe, in 1505 and another one is a mention of a bismuth mine in Saxony in an official list of mines and their estimated values dating back to 1477.

[6] In an earlier book, *Bermannus,* printed in 1530, Agricola said in so many words that the metal called *bisemutum* was unknown to the ancients and that there are more than seven metals.

The miners, it may be mentioned, had their own ideas on "transmutation." They thought that lead slowly changed into tin, tin into bismuth and bismuth into silver, and it is reported that one mining master, when the ore turned out to be bismuth, exclaimed: "Alas, we have come too soon." But even the disappointed mining master who had hoped for silver, knew that bismuth was salable. The artisans who made tin platters, pitchers, etc., added bismuth to make the metal harder, and bismuth became a needed commodity after the invention of printing. Johann Gutenberg and his associate, Peter Schöffer, who developed printing from movable type, had found that a mixture of only tin and lead was not hard enough for the purpose, so bismuth was added. In 1495 the first printer in Spain ordered 77 pounds of bismuth from Germany for his type. And in about 1530 the German mastersinger and poet, Hans Sachs, wrote two lines for a woodcut that portrayed the casting of type:

> I pour the type for the printing shop,
> Made well of wissmat, tin and bob [lead].

In spite of Agricola's clear description, as well as the wide usage of the metal, the French Academy still maintained in 1713 that bismuth was a mixture of tin, arsenic, raw sulphur and earth. Considering that it was the French Academy that doubted the nature of the metal, it was perhaps poetic justice that a French chemist, Claude-François Geoffrey, published a research paper in 1753 on bismuth, showing clearly that it was a distinct metal.

IV. A COLLECTION OF GASES

One of the favorite operations of the alchemists was a process they called "calcining." It consisted of placing a mineral or a metal into a crucible and heating it until nothing was left but a powdery solid. Since this powdery solid evidently had resisted prolonged heating better than anything else, it was believed to have special "virtues" and was called "calx," as, for example, the calx of arsenic. Calcining, incidentally, provided further proof of the superiority of gold because gold did not have a calx.

In 1489 a German alchemist, Eck von Sulzbach, made the startling discovery that the calx of a metal weighed more than the metal before calcining. The only explanation he could think of was that a "ghost" had come from somewhere and moved into the calx, thereby increasing its weight.

We now know that Eck von Sulzbach had come close to the truth. Calcining a metal means, in present-day terminology, to oxidize it with the oxygen in the atmosphere and naturally the compound of metal plus oxygen will weigh more than the metal itself. But the fifteenth-century alchemist could not arrive at this conclusion because Aristotle, whose word was still undisputed, had said that air was an element that did not combine with metals. However, the time was not far off when this statement was to be questioned.

The first man to say that air could not be an element was the artist, sculptor, early engineer and all-around genius, Leonardo da Vinci (1452–1519). He had noticed that air is consumed by breathing or by burning something, but that not all of it is consumed. This meant to Leonardo that air consisted of at least two substances, one of which was consumed while the other was not. The Englishman, Robert Hooke (1635–1703), went into more detail. In 1665 he stated that air consists of an active and an inert substance. The inert substance, he wrote, exists in a larger quantity than the active substance and the latter also exists in solid form in saltpeter.

The description was almost perfect. The inert gas (nitrogen) is four times as abundant in the atmosphere as the active gas (oxygen) and, while saltpeter is not solid oxygen, it is a salt from which a great deal of oxygen can be released by heating. Unfortunately little attention was paid to Hooke's explanation. This may have been partly due to the fact that it was hidden in a book devoted to studies with the microscope and adorned with many beautiful illustrations. But Hooke had the deserved reputation of engaging in needless arguments and arbitrary discussions—and statements by a constantly bickering man are likely to be disregarded. In that respect Hooke had the same fate as Paracelsus and for much the same reason.

If Hooke had been a more agreeable man and a more

thorough researcher, the ridiculous "phlogiston theory" of the two Germans, Johann Joachim Becher (1635–1682) and Georg Ernst Stahl (1660–1734), would never even have found a hearing. Both men were chemists and physicians, Stahl being quite famous in the latter field. Becher had conceived the idea of phlogiston while Stahl, born twenty-five years later, enlarged on and popularized it after Becher's death.

The theory had started out logically enough. All kinds of things could be burned; it did not matter whether they were large or small, round or uneven in form, heavy like coal or light like hay. Even their color did not matter. Hence the process of burning had to be something that had no relation to anything else. There had to be a special substance that was responsible for burning; Stahl and Becher called it "phlogiston," from the Greek word, *phlogistein,* "to burn away." A metal contained phlogiston; if it was calcined, the phlogiston escaped and the calx was left behind. Therefore, the calx was a simpler substance than the metal. And the reason that a metal calx was heavier than the metal alone was explained by the fact that phlogiston was the only substance with "levity," the only substance which had a negative weight. Having driven the phlogiston from the metal by heating it, its lifting "influence" had been removed, too, so naturally the calx weighed more. Of course, neither Becher nor Stahl could show a sample of phlogiston because it could not be made pure. It had been observed, for example, that combustion stopped after a while when a candle was burned in a closed space. We know that the candle goes out because all the oxygen in the closed space has been used up; Becher and Stahl, however, explained that air was necessary during combustion because it served as a sponge for the released phlogiston, absorbing it. But it could absorb only so much;

once the air was saturated with phlogiston, combustion had to stop.

Even during Stahl's lifetime chemists might have cited examples that could not be explained by that theory, but Stahl had become the personal physician to King Friedrich I of Prussia and his word carried weight accordingly.

Actually the phlogiston theory did not prevent the discovery of new elements but it explains some of the very strange terminology used by other chemists of the period.

The first of the elementary gases to be discovered was hydrogen, and its discoverer was Henry Cavendish (1731–1810). Descended from the Dukes of Kent and the Dukes of Devonshire, Cavendish, by way of inheriting the fortunes of elderly relatives who died, became a very rich man and was for a number of years the largest depositor in the Bank of England. He was not only rich, but also incredibly shy, preferring to speak only to one person at a time and that person had to be a man. Actually, he disclaimed the discovery of hydrogen, saying, "It has been observed by others." That was true, as others had observed it, but Cavendish was the first man to find a way of collecting it. To do so, he used mercury, which formed a kind of flexible seal over a container. Cavendish could introduce gas into the bottom of a container thus sealed, and the gas could not escape through the mercury. This work was done in 1766, now regarded as the year of the discovery of hydrogen. Cavendish's name for the gas was "inflammable air from metals" because it was obtained by treating metals with acids. (Actually the hydrogen was a constituent of the acids, not of the metals.)

Cavendish determined the specific weight of his inflammable air and found it to be only 1/11 of that of ordinary air, which is quite accurate as we know. But then he did something far more important. Knowing that his "air" was inflammable, he burned some of it in ordinary air in a closed container to see what the product of this reaction might be. Since he was not given to vivid writing we have no record of the immense surprise he must have felt when he saw that the product was water. He repeated the experiment several times, finding that one fifth of the ordinary air disappeared and that the weight of the water formed was equal to the weight of his inflammable air plus one fifth of the ordinary air. He first reported on these experiments in a private letter to Joseph Priestley in 1781. Soon it was common knowledge among chemists. The great French chemist, Antoine Laurent Lavoisier, in Paris repeated the experiments and lectured about them on November 21, 1782.

Lavoisier was mainly interested in demolishing the idea that water was an element. But his lecture had an unexpected by-product. One professor, Jacques A. C. Charles, suggested that this newly discovered hydrogen would be far superior to heated air to carry a balloon up into the atmosphere and the first flight of a hydrogen-filled balloon took place in 1783.

Cavendish's work on hydrogen had destroyed one of the "elements" of antiquity, namely water. Air was the next; but the recognition that it was a mixture of gases was the outcome of the work of many men. Nearly a century earlier the Flemish physician, Jan Baptista van Helmont (1577–1644), declared that the "air" resulting from the burning of wood was different from ordinary air. Although Helmont still believed in the four "elements," or rather *because* he still believed in them, he coined a new word. Substances like the "element earth" were called "solids"; substances like the "element water" were called "liquids." But there was no word for substances like "air." The word he coined for such substances was "gas," based on the Greek word *chaos*, which in its original language means "unformed." Too bad that nobody used the word "gas" until it was reintroduced by Lavoisier a hundred and fifty years later.

Thirty years after van Helmont's death, an English physician, John Mayow, wrote a treatise which *almost,* but only almost, proved that the "element air" consists of two different gases.

The actual discovery of the composition of air was the work of six remarkable men, of whom Cavendish was one. The others were Joseph Black, Daniel Rutherford, Joseph Priestley, Karl Scheele, and Antoine Lavoisier.

Joseph Black (1728–1799) was a Scottish physician and professor of chemistry at Glasgow. He discovered carbon dioxide, which he called "fixed air," and encouraged his pupil, Daniel Rutherford, to experiment in the same field. Daniel Rutherford (1749–1819) also was a Scottish physician and chemist who became professor of botany at Edinburgh. Rutherford, incidentally, was the uncle of the famous novelist, Sir Walter Scott. His discovery of nitrogen, which he called "noxious air," was made in 1772. Joseph Priestley (1733–1804) was an English clergyman who wrote a book entitled *Experiments and Observations on Different Kinds of Air*. In the history of science he is celebrated as one of the discoverers of oxygen, but he also made an important invention that is mentioned less often. He experimented with nitrogen and carbon dioxide, and it so happened that his home was near a brewery where he could obtain carbon dioxide in almost unlimited quantities. He was still working on the problem of which gases could be kept over water in a container and which had to be kept over mercury when he found that carbon dioxide would dissolve in water. Tasting the water, as part of his routine examinations, he found the taste very refreshing and induced several of his friends to taste it, too. This was the beginning of the carbonated beverages industry. Priestley died in the United States. Karl

Wilhelm Scheele (1742–1786) was born in Stralsund, then the capital of Swedish Pomerania. But while Scheele was a Swedish subject, all his writings are in German. He worked mainly in Sweden, starting as an apothecary's apprentice. His work, *Über die Luft und das Feuer* (About Air and Combustion), was started in 1771. Along with Priestley, Scheele is considered the discoverer of oxygen. Both Scheele and Priestley did their work independently and at the same time, but Priestley's work was published earlier than Scheele's.

While these men, among them, cleared up the mystery of the "element air," Cavendish, Black, Rutherford, and Priestley were all adherents of the phlogiston theory; Priestley, in fact, always referred to oxygen as "dephlogisticated air." His belief still was that this kind of "air," since it did not yet contain any phlogiston at all, supported combustion so well because it was ready to receive the phlogiston that would be released by the burning substance.

The man who finally demolished the phlogiston theory was the Frenchman, Antoine Laurent Lavoisier, who was born in 1743. He was the son of a lawyer and became a public official, a tax collector. Although Lavoisier did not discover a single element, he is regarded as the "father of modern chemistry." Lavoisier established a very strict technique of chemical analysis and cleaned up chemical terminology (which was still suffering from alchemical terminology), and he established a new system of naming chemical compounds that is still largely in use. And he was a sworn enemy of phlogiston. "That substance," he said, "is sometimes endowed with 'levity' and at other times it has weight; sometimes it can penetrate a brick and sometimes it cannot. It has all kinds of wonderful attributes to which I shall add another one, I am going to show that it is just a figment of the imagination."

He did just that. He showed that combustion was a combination of the combustible substance with oxygen, not the escape of phlogiston. He also showed that the weight of *every* substance that could be burned increased in the process, because oxygen had been added. He explained why combustion often *seemed* to cause a loss of weight as in the case of charcoal ashes, which weigh much less than the original charcoal. The product of burning charcoal is mainly carbon dioxide and this gas had been permitted to escape by earlier experimenters. Lavoisier proved that the ashes plus the carbon dioxide weighed more than the original charcoal.

Unfortunately for Lavoisier, he was an important government official in the French kingdom, and his beautiful and intelligent wife was the daughter of another government official. During the French Revolution he was branded "an enemy of the people" and was executed in 1794. His request to be permitted to conclude an investigation he had started was refused with the words: "The Republic does not need scientists!"

One more gaseous element was discovered during this period, namely chlorine. Karl Wilhelm Scheele had noticed it in the course of his experiments and he called it "dephlogisticated muriatic acid," not recognizing it as an element. The great French chemist, Count Claude Louis Berthollet (1748–1822), who collaborated with Lavoisier, thought that chlorine was a compound of hydrochloric acid and oxygen. Nobody thought that it might be an element and that was the fault of the great Lavoisier. At one point in his researches, Lavoisier had come to the conclusion that every acid has to contain oxygen. That happens to be wrong; most acids do contain oxygen but not all of them. And one of the exceptions is the rather common hydrochloric acid.

In order to recognize chlorine as an element it first had to be proved that there were acids that do not contain oxygen.[1] It was Sir Humphry Davy of England (1778–1829) who showed that hydrochloric acid did not contain oxygen but consisted only of chlorine and hydrogen. Hydrogen was known to be an element and chlorine, which had successfully resisted all attempts to break it down, therefore had to be an element, too. Sir Humphry Davy made the crucial experiment in 1807, but it was another dozen years before all chemists were so convinced.

[1] But all acids do contain hydrogen.

V. NEW METALS

There exists a fairly common mineral that attracted the attention of medieval miners because it was so heavy. Because of its great weight the German-speaking miners called it "*Schwerspat*," the English equivalent is "heavy spar." It was also called "baryta," from the Greek *barys*, "heavy." Around the year 1600 baryta acquired brief fame because a shoemaker in Bologna, Vincenzo Casciarolo, trying to extract gold from it, found that it could be made to glow in the dark after it had been exposed to sunlight.

The heaviness of the mineral did seem to indicate that a heavy metal was hidden within it and the early chemists tried to find out what it was, though without success. Lavoisier, writing in 1780, said, "It is quite probable that baryta . . . is an oxide of a metal. It is even possible that all the earths are just metal oxides, but the means at our disposal are insufficient for their reduction." In principle, Lavoisier was correct, except that the mineral was not an oxide of the unknown metal, but a sulphur compound. And in order to obtain it, something was needed that was not yet known in Lavoisier's time, namely, electric current.

At the same time Lavoisier set down his beliefs, Karl Wilhelm Scheele in Sweden investigated heavy spar by heating a paste made of the mineral ground up, pulverized charcoal, and honey. He then dissolved the result in hydrochloric acid and added potassium carbonate,[1] but he did not obtain the metal he was hoping for. The result was what is called "barium carbonate." The first man to obtain metallic barium, the metal actually in the heavy spar, was Sir Humphry Davy in 1808.

Of course, the metal from baryta was called "barium," but there was a difficulty. The mineral had attracted attention because of its weight, but the metal barium was not particularly heavy, weighing only 3.78 times as much as the same

[1] The term "carbonate" indicates that the metal forms a chemical compound with carbon, just as the term "oxide" indicates that the metal forms a compound with oxygen. Most chemical terms are constructed in this manner; a "sulphate" is a compound of a metal with sulphur, an "arsenide" is a compound with arsenic, a "phosphate" is a compound with phosphorus, while a "hydride" is a compound with hydrogen, and a "nitrate" is a compound with nitrogen. But terms like "sulphate-sulphide," "phosphate-phosphide," "chlorate-chloride" and so forth are not interchangeable, for they indicate different proportions in the compound. It may be added here that there are some simple compounds that behave as if they were metals when forming more complicated compounds with other elements. The best known example of such a simple compound is ammonia, consisting of one atom of nitrogen and three of hydrogen, hence written NH_3.

The term "to reduce," used by Lavoisier, means to decompose an oxide of a metal. In most cases this can be accomplished by heating a metal oxide with charcoal, that is, carbon. Oxygen has a greater tendency to combine with carbon than with some metals; hence the metal oxide is split into metal and oxygen, the oxygen combines with the carbon, and the metal is left behind. Agricola's description of obtaining bismuth is an example of such a "reduction."

volume of water. For this reason E. D. Clarke, who had just been appointed professor of chemistry at Cambridge when Davy made metallic barium, suggested that it should be given another name. Because the metal came from underground, he said, "plutonium" would be a suitable name, free of any associations with the Greek word for "heavy." Some chemists went along with the suggestion, but since it is traditionally the discoverer who names his discovery and since Sir Humphry Davy had called the metal "barium," barium it remained. (For the modern plutonium, see Chapter X.)

The story of barium also shows why it is often difficult to say who discovered a new element. Should the credit go to Lavoisier, who guessed that the compound consisted of a nonmetal and an unknown metal? Or should it go to Scheele, whose investigation indicated that the compounds he obtained differed from other known compounds? Or should it go to Davy, who was the first to obtain the metal in practically pure form?

In this particular case, Sir Humphry Davy is usually listed as the discoverer. But in other cases the chemist who could convincingly prove that he had a compound of a new element might be credited as its discoverer, even though he did not personally succeed in isolating it.

This last sentence applies to several discoveries of the German chemist, Martin Heinrich Klaproth (1743–1817), born at Wernigerode in the Harz mountains. A fire destroyed all the possessions of the family and young Martin Heinrich, at the age of fifteen, became apprenticed to an apothecary in Quedlinburg. (He later complained that his master never taught him anything.) Eight years later he became "helper" at the Court Pharmacy in Hanover and, after another two years, he moved to Berlin and to the Golden Angel Pharmacy. After a short absence from the city, he found a place in the Swan Pharmacy in Berlin, owned and founded by Valentin Rose (1735–1771). Valentin Rose had founded more than a pharmacy; he had also founded a dynasty of chemists. His son, Valentin Rose the Younger (1762–1807) was a distinguished chemist and pharmacist, and his son, Heinrich Rose (1795–1864), did important work in distinguishing two very similar metals, namely, tantalum and niobium, as will be told later.

Valentin Rose the Elder was much impressed by Klaproth, who was twenty-eight years old at the time. Feeling that he would die soon, Rose willed the pharmacy to Klaproth under the condition that he would take care of his two sons—the younger of which died early—and educate them. Klaproth and the younger Valentin Rose became lifelong friends and collaborated on many chemical investigations.

Klaproth's year of glory was 1789, and the source of the glory was, the silver mine of St. Joachimsthal in Bohemia that had been started a few centuries earlier.[2] But the mine not only yielded silver, but also quantities of a mineral that looked like hardened pitch and was called "pitchblende." Chemists thought that it might be a mixture of zinc and iron ores, but when Klaproth, as the first step of a chemical analysis, dissolved it in nitric acid, it became clear immediately that neither iron nor zinc was present. He obtained a yellowish substance and suspected that this was a compound of a new element. Trying to obtain the element in its pure form, he produced a black powder that looked metallic. Klaproth thought that this was the new element and he named it "uranium," in honor of Sir William Herschel's discovery of the planet Uranus in 1781. Much later, the French chemist,

[2] The name means "St. Joachim's Dale" and in 1519 the Austrian government appointed one Count von Schlick overseer of the mine. Under his direction large silver coins were minted which circulated internationally under the name of *Joachimsthaler*. The name was soon shortened into *Thaler,* or *Daler,* and finally became "dollar."

Péligot, proved that Klaproth's uranium metal was actually the oxide of the metal and in 1841 obtained the true uranium metal for the first time. But Klaproth is considered the discoverer of uranium.

During the same year Klaproth discovered another element. Among the gemstones there is one known as "jacinth," "hyacinth" or "zircon," yellow to reddish in color. Klaproth examined a pale specimen from Ceylon and noticed that it had an unusually high weight, 4.615 times as heavy as water. He decided to analyze it and found a new "earth" with a new element which he called "zirconium." He could not isolate the metal, nor were most later efforts successful. Pure zirconium was not made until 1924.

In addition to finding two new elements, Klaproth became the codiscoverer of three others, strontium, titanium and chromium.

Strontianite, the mineral containing strontium, was found in a Scottish mine but was confused with another mineral, called "witherite" after a Birmingham physician, Dr. Withering. In modern terminology witherite is barium carbonate, which does look very much like strontianite. Around the year 1787 several researchers began to make a distinction between the minerals. Two physicians in Scotland, Dr. John Ash (1723–1798) and Dr. William Cruikshank (1745–1800), pointed out that witherite, thrown into a fire, colored the flame green, while strontianite colored the flame bright red. At the same time the German physician, Dr. Friedrich Gabriel Sulzer (1749–1830), wrote a letter to the famous anatomist, Johann Friedrich Blumenbach (1752–1840), in which he stated that strontianite could not be a barium compound. It was lighter than witherite, dissolved more easily, produced crystals of different shape, and, as experiments with animals had shown, it did not seem to be poisonous.

Klaproth checked all the statements (except for animal experiments) and determined that witherite had a specific gravity of 4.300 while strontianite had one of only 3.675. Klaproth's attempt to reduce the strontianite to the metal by heating it in a closed crucible failed; afterwards, he always found the strontianite unchanged. We now know that his furnace simply was not hot enough to reduce the mineral. The first to obtain the pure metal was Robert Bunsen, around the middle of the nineteenth century.

Titanium, was first discovered by an Anglican minister by the name of William Gregor (1761–1817). He was born in Cornwall and lived there most of his life, and, in addition to his regular occupation, he became known as a landscape painter and musician. Also interested in chemistry, Gregor wondered about a black sand from the valley of Menacchan in Cornwall. After treating it with acids, evaporating the acid and heating the residue, he obtained a very light white powder that he believed contained a new element. The powder must have been titanium oxide, probably containing some iron.

About a year later Klaproth was asked to analyze a mineral found in Hungary that was labeled "Hungarian red schörl." After trying everything he could think of, Klaproth was convinced that he was dealing with a compound of a new element, and, in 1795, he named the unknown metal "titanium." But no one knew what pure titanium looked like until 1910 when the American chemist, M. A. Hunter, heated titanium tetrachloride with sodium in a closed pressure container. An investigation of the metal showed that it had almost incredible characteristics. Its specific weight was only 4.5 but it was almost as strong as steel (with a specific weight of 7.8), had high elasticity, did not corrode, and could be stretched into fine filaments like those in light bulbs. The only drawback of this "wonder metal" was that it seemed to be rare, until large deposits were found in Canada. It now is used as the outer skin of high-flying aircraft and space-going devices.

The element chromium was discovered in 1798 and the French chemist, Nicolas-Louis Vauquelin (1763–1829), apothecary at first and later professor of chemistry in Paris, is considered to be its discoverer. Klaproth also tried to analyze the substance at the same time, but he had only a limited supply of the mineral and was quite willing to have Vauquelin carry the investigation to a conclusion. The material went under the name of "Siberian red lead" even though it came from Russia and not Siberia. Vauquelin, in a first analysis in 1789, had found lead, iron, alum and much oxygen in the compound. A German chemist working in Moscow, Bindheim, said that Vauquelin was completely wrong, and that Siberian red lead contained copper, cobalt, nickel, iron and a compound of molybdenum.

The obvious result was that Vauquelin wanted to try again, while Klaproth, sitting on the sidelines, felt that he might be able to unravel the puzzle mainly because, so far, he had not paid any attention to the mineral. Klaproth first pulverized the material and then dropped it into a glass containing hydrochloric acid. He obtained a yellow solution. Then he boiled the solution and it turned emerald green. White crystals of lead chloride formed simultaneously at the bottom of the container. Then Klaproth added soda and the solution turned a different shade of green.

By that time his small sample was exhausted, but Klaproth was convinced that this must be a new element, as no other element was known to produce such a display of colors.

Nicolas-Louis Vauquelin, having a larger supply made available to him by the French government, noticed all the color changes that Klaproth had seen. In addition to the colored solutions, he also obtained two colored precipitates,[3] one cinnabar red and one strongly yellow. Then he tried to reduce the oxide of the new element to the pure metal by heating it with charcoal. It worked, and his crucible was filled with metallic threads. Vauquelin's teacher, Antoine-François de Fourcroy, suggested the name. No other element produced so many colors; Greek for "color" is *chroma,* hence chromium.

Vauquelin discovered another element, the one now known as "beryllium."

Beryl is a gemstone like emerald and because the two stones differ in color nobody had ever connected the two. A French mineralogist, however, the Abbé Haüy, noticed that their crystal structures were identical and suggested to Vauquelin that he make a chemical analysis. An emerald from Peru had already been analyzed by Klaproth, who had received the stone for this purpose from Prince Dimitri Galitzin of Russia. He found it to contain 31.25 percent alumina, 66.25 percent silica and 0.5 percent iron oxide.

What Klaproth called "alumina" actually had been a new compound, and Vauquelin, in his first analysis of a beryl, made the same mistake. But then he found chemical differences, one of them being that the "salts" of the unknown element had a sweet taste.

In February 1798 he reported to the French Academy that he had found a new "earth" and had named it "*glucina*"

[3] A precipitate is a substance that will form at the bottom of a container when certain chemicals are added to a solution. The knowledge as to which chemicals will cause such a result is of the greatest importance to analytical chemists.

("sweet"); but Klaproth, pointing out that other elements can also form sweet-tasting compounds, labeled Vauquelin's substance "beryllia." The metal beryllium was isolated by Friedrich Wöhler (whose accomplishments will be discussed in the next chapter) precisely thirty years after the discovery of beryllia. Vauquelin was a bit disturbed because neither Torbern Bergman in Sweden nor Bindheim in Moscow, both of whom had reported analyses of beryls, had found his *glucina*. But later it turned out that both scientists had entrusted the actual analysis to their pupils, who did not have enough experience to recognize a new substance.

Among the elements discovered during the thirty-odd years from 1777 (the year Lavoisier disproved the phlogiston theory) and about 1812, molybdenum must be mentioned next.

Three different ores, those now called "molybdenite," "graphite"[4] and "galena" (lead ore), had all been thought to be the same because they looked alike. In 1778 Karl Wilhelm Scheele, after treating molybdenite with nitric acid, obtained a white powder which he called "water-lead earth," the reason for the name being that it dissolved easily in water while the true lead compound dissolves only very slowly. Scheele's friend, Peter Jakob Hjelm (1746–1813), tried to isolate the element but Hjelm, being assay master of the Royal Mint, was a busy man and did not get around to it until 1790, four years after Scheele's death. Though he did make some progress, it would be wrong to say that he was successful. He wasn't and several others had to give up, too.

The metal molybdenum was not isolated until 1817, by Berzelius.

[4] Graphite is uncrystallized carbon and was called "Spanish lead" for a long time. It is because of this name that we still speak of "lead" pencils.

The metal wolfram—formerly called "tungsten" in the English-speaking countries—came to its name in a strange manner. Among tin ores another ore was usually found. The men who smelted the tin ore tried to remove this foreign ore before smelting the tin. This unwanted ore prevented some of the tin ore from giving up its metal and the miners said: "It carries the tin away and swallows it as a wolf swallows a sheep." The saying led to calling the ore "wolfert." Gradually the word changed into "wolfram." The point to remember is that the term "wolfram" then meant the ore, not the metal in that ore. Nowadays, "wolfram" means the metal, while the ore is called "wolframite"; another wolfram ore is called "scheelite" after Karl Wilhelm Scheele, who began investigating it in 1781. Scheele had another name for it, one that was used by Swedish miners. They called the white mineral "*tung sten*" or "heavy stone," but it was not the same as the "heavy spar" of their German counterparts, the ore that finally yielded barium.

Scheele found that the "heavy stone" was a compound of lime and of another solid to which he gave the name of "tungstic acid." Scheele's friend, Torbern Bergman, felt certain that it contained a metal, probably an unknown one.

At that point two Spaniards entered the picture, the brothers de Elhuyar. Don Fausto de Elhuyar (1755–1833), who was to become more famous than his bother, Juan José, had been born in Logroño in northern Spain. The King of Spain, knowing that his country needed mining experts and mineralogists, sent the brothers to Germany and to Sweden for study. In Sweden they became the pupils of Bergman, who praised their diligence. The two brothers first established that the Swedish *tung sten* and the German "wolfram" contained the same "tungstic acid" that Scheele had named. In time they tried to obtain the metal and succeeded in 1783.

At first the new metal was only a scientific curiosity, but later, during the nineteenth century, it was found that an addition of wolfram to iron produced a very superior steel and the metal that the tin miners had hated became the favorite of the steelmakers.

The brothers de Elhuyar returned to their native country after finishing their studies in Sweden, but they did not stay long. Don Juan José was sent to organize and supervise the mines in Colombia (he died in Bogotá in 1804) while Don Fausto did the same in Mexico. He returned to Spain after and absence of thirty-three years in 1825 and was appointed Minister of Mines, a position he filled until his death.

One of Scheele's numerous scientific friends was the chemist and mining engineer, Johann Gottlieb Gahn (1745–1818). Gahn was born in Voxna, an iron-mining town, and because his father died at a comparatively young age, the teen-age Gahn became a miner. Somehow he succeeded in studying under Bergman, met Scheele, who was then an apothecary at Upsala, and, in 1770, obtained a position at the Swedish College of Mining. He also became a Deputy in the Swedish Parliament. When he lectured and experimented, the young Berzelius watched him avidly; later Berzelius and Gahn bought a sulphuric-acid factory at Gripsholm. Unfortunately we don't know much about the things Gahn did; he did not publish much because he said that he would write about his life and work after his retirement. But he died suddenly and the book, which no doubt would have been very interesting, remained unwritten.

However, we do know how Gahn discovered the metal manganese in 1774, taking over from his friend, Scheele, who had worked on the problem without success. The ore in which the new metal was found went under several names, the most common of which translates into English simply as "brownstone." [5]

Pliny knew of it because he mentioned the fact that, when added to liquid glass, it removes any coloration the glass might have because of other minerals. But Pliny thought that it was magnetic iron ore, or lodestone. It so happens that it does not contain iron at all and it is very likely that Pliny never saw brownstone and lodestone side by side. To justify Pliny's statement, the alchemists invented a distinction between "male" and "female" lodestones; the latter, of course, were the weaker.

The first man we know of who stated that there was no iron in brownstone was Johann Heinrich Pott in Berlin (in 1740). Professionally he was a glass and porcelain maker and was therefore well acquainted with minerals. Then Bergman and Scheele took over, Bergman saying that the ability of brownstone to clear glass indicated the presence of a metal, but his efforts to obtain it failed and he asked Scheele to carry on. Scheele did, but after some time he turned the problem over to Gahn. Gahn took a crucible and filled it with moistened charcoal, put a lump of paste of pulverized brownstone and oil in the center and covered the whole with pulverized charcoal. Then he heated the crucible for an hour in a very hot furnace. After it had cooled enough to be handled, Gahn found a piece of a metal that weighed one third of the weight of the mineral he had made into paste.

It is now known that Gahn may not have been the first to obtain metallic manganese. There exists a dissertation by an Austrian named Ignatius Gottfried Kaim, dated 1700. It describes a very similar process with the same mineral, but Kaim failed to describe the characteristics of the metal he

[5] This is not the same as the "brownstone" of many old houses in New York City. The name of the mineral is derived from the fact that it turns brown in a hot fire.

obtained, so that Gahn is still considered the discoverer of manganese.

Ytterby is a little town not far from Stockholm which now has the unique distinction of having no fewer than four different elements named after it. It all started in 1788 when Lieutenant Carl Axel Arrhenius of the Swedish army picked up a piece of mineral near a mine. It made him curious because it was very black and very heavy. He passed it on to a Mr. Geyer, the chief of the mine, who, in turn, sent it to Klaproth. The sample was too small for a complete analysis but Klaproth could say that it was different from anything he had ever seen before.

A few years later Johan Gadolin (1760–1852), a pupil of Bergman and professor of chemistry at the University of Åbo, Finland, went to work on a larger sample. After a long series of tests he could state that the black mineral contained 38 percent of an unknown "earth." Then Anders Gustaf Ekeberg (1767–1813), chemist at the University of Upsala, continued Gadolin's observations, starting out with a full hundred pounds of raw material. He confirmed Gadolin's findings and, in 1799, suggested that the black mineral should be named "gadolinite" in his honor and gadolinite it has been ever since. As for the "earth" isolated by Gadolin, Ekeberg said that it should be named after the place where Lieutenant Arrhenius had picked up the first sample: "ytter-earth," or "yttria." The unknown metal in yttria, namely "yttrium," was not isolated until nearly half a century later, by Friedrich Wöhler.

The discovery of yttria opened the way to finding a whole series of elements collectively known as the "rare-earth elements" or "the lanthanides" (see Chapter VIII). The first of these rare-earth elements made its appearance very soon; it was found in the "heavy spar of Bastnäs" which was examined in 1803 by three different men independently. They were Klaproth, Berzelius and Wilhelm von Hisinger, a Swedish nobleman who was born in December 1766 at Riddarhyttan, the birthplace of Georg Brandt. All three of them found that this Swedish heavy spar contained an unknown material instead of the yttria they had expected to find. Berzelius suggested the name "cerite" for it, while Klaproth called it *"terre ochroite"* ("brownish soil"). Some busybodies whispered that Klaproth had known about the work of Berzelius when he published his own analysis. Klaproth was understandably annoyed and blamed Berzelius, but Berzelius himself had no knowledge of the accusation, it having been made without even asking him. Strangely enough the unpleasant story had a pleasing outcome for Berzelius, who was only twenty-four years old at the time. It called attention to his name in scientific circles.

Berzelius then went on to find cerite in a number of other minerals, while both Gahn and Vauquelin tried to isolate the metal in the cerite. Both were equally unsuccessful. The Swedish chemist, Carl Gustaf Mosander—affectionately known as Papa Moses to his pupils—and Friedrich Wöhler succeeded to some extent. Both obtained the metal, although it was very impure and they could not find a way of purifying it. Nearly pure cerium was prepared for the first time by two American chemists, Thomas H. Norton of the University of Cincinnati and William F. Hillebrand of the U.S. Geological Survey, who collaborated on the problem in 1875.

Cerium, alloyed with iron, can now be found in the pockets of many men and in the pocketbooks of almost as many ladies, for this alloy is the substance that forms the "flint" in a cigarette lighter.

Not every new element was discovered in Sweden or in Swedish ores. Franz Josef Müller von Reichenstein (1740–

1825) was an Austrian, born in Hermannstadt in Transylvania, then part of the Austro-Hungarian Empire. (Now the area belongs to Rumania and the city is named Sibiu.) Having been a good student in Vienna and an efficient administrator in several minor posts, he was finally appointed chief inspector of all the government-owned mines in Transylvania. In 1782 Müller von Reichenstein extracted a metal from the ores of a mine under his supervision—the mine had the name of Mariahilf—which he first thought to be antimony. But a more careful investigation convinced him that it was not antimony, but something he did not know. Thinking that it might be known elsewhere, he sent a small sample to Torbern Bergman, but all Bergman could do with it was to confirm that it was not antimony. Müller von Reichenstein then published a paper about his discovery, although for a long time no one paid any attention to it.

In 1789 a Hungarian professor by the name of Paul Kitaibel discovered a new element in silver ores from Pilsen in Czechoslovakia. It was the same element Müller von Reichenstein had discovered, but apparently Kitaibel had never heard about the metal from the Mariahilf mine. He seems to have felt somewhat uncertain about his own discovery, for, though he wrote a report about it, he did not have it published, only mentioning it to a few friends. One of these friends, the mineralogist Estner in Vienna, had a copy of the report and showed it to Klaproth when the latter paid a visit to Vienna in 1796. Klaproth read it and stated in writing that it was a good piece of work. But Klaproth also knew about Müller von Reichenstein's paper and got in touch with its author, asking for mineral from the Mariahilf mine. Müller von Reichenstein replied that the ore was becoming rare, but he supplied Klaproth with enough of it for an analysis. In a paper he read to the Academy of Sciences in Berlin in January 1798, Klaproth described precisely what he had done.[6] The ore was mined for its gold content but contained, in addition to gold, iron and the new element. In his paper Klaproth proposed the name "tellurium" for the new element (from Latin *tellus,* the earth). Some historians, impressed by the relatively simple manner in which Klaproth had obtained the new metal, have called him the discoverer of tellurium. But in his paper Klaproth stressed that it had been Müller von Reichenstein; all he had done was to demonstrate to his own satisfaction that it existed and he claimed credit only for having named it.

John Winthrop the Younger (1606–1676), first governor of Connecticut, was a physician, an alchemist and a mineral collector. Some time during his career, around the year 1650, he found an interesting piece of mineral in a spring near New London, Connecticut, and took it home with him. Many years later Winthrop's grandson sent it to England to Sir Hans Sloane, the founder of the British Museum, where it continued to rest undisturbed. In 1801, or about a century and a half after it had been found, the English chemist and manufacturer, Charles Hatchett (*c.*1765–1847), became interested in it and went to work. In November 1801 he presented a paper to the Royal Society with the title: "Analysis of a Mineral from North America Containing a Metal Hith-

[6] The three metals in the ore were imbedded in quartz; Klaproth pulverized the ore and dissolved the powder in *aqua regis* (a mixture of nitric and sulphuric acids), which could be counted upon to dissolve everything, except the quartz. Meanwhile he had dissolved mercury in cold nitric acid; the mercury would remove the gold by forming an amalgam. Then he added potassium hydroxide, which caused the iron to form a compound that precipitated. By then, Klaproth had a solution free of gold and iron, but still containing the tellurium. This solution was alkaline, so Klaproth added hydrochloric acid until the solution was perfectly neutralized. This resulted in a white precipitate, tellurium oxide. After drying, the oxide was gently heated with charcoal, the oxygen from the metal oxide combined with the carbon of the charcoal to form carbon dioxide, which was permitted to escape, and metallic tellurium was left behind.

erto Unknown." Because the mineral had come from the New World, Hatchett called it "columbite" and the new metal would have been called "columbium." But while the discovery of the presence of a new metal proved that Hatchett was an excellent chemist, he did not succeed in isolating it.[7]

In 1802, at the time that Hatchett presented his paper to the Royal Society, Ekeberg in Sweden found an element that, surprisingly, acids could not attack. Greek mythology tells about Tantalus, who offended the gods and was condemned to be forever thirsty; but while he was standing more than waist-deep in water he could not quench his thirst, for every time he bent down to drink, the water receded. The fact that his new metal could not "drink" the acids made Ekeberg call it "tantalum." The mineral in question acquired the name of "tantalite."

Chemists were naturally interested in Hatchett's columbium, which nobody had yet seen, and in 1809 William Hyde Wollaston, the discoverer of rhodium and palladium, suddenly declared that Hatchett's columbium and Ekeberg's tantalum were one and the same metal. He admitted that there were differences in specific weight, but thought that this was due to impurities. The real problem was one that Wollaston could not yet recognize, which was that the two metals almost invariably occur together. The man who succeded in finding the answer after other chemists, including even Wöhler, had given up was Heinrich Rose, the grandson of the founder of the Swan Pharmacy in Berlin.

Rose began his work on the minerals containing tantalum in 1840; the complete investigation took not less than twenty years. In 1844 he isolated the metal in Hatchett's columbite and the one who was especially pleased about this was Wöhler, who had tried it without success. "I do not grieve

[7] The mineral columbite also contains tantalum, titanium, wolfram, zirconium, cerium, yttrium and thorium, all of them in different compounds.

that it escaped me," he wrote to Berzelius, "and I grant the discovery with a happy heart to the good Heinrich." Rose, the "good Heinrich," not only discovered the new element but also proved that it was not the same as tantalum, though the two are always associated. Because of this steady association he called the metal "niobium," since, in legend, Niobe was the daughter of Tantalus. "Niobium" was accepted and "columbium" officially dropped by the International Chemical Union a number of years ago.

But now we must return to the early years of the nineteenth century. A young Irishman by the name of Richard Chevenix was walking the streets of London when he was given a handbill stating that the merchant Forster in Soho—a section of London—had a new metal for sale. Since Chevenix was a chemist, the offer interested him. He made the trip to Soho and bought a small piece, though it seems that he had made up his mind in advance that it probably would prove to be some known metal. But the few tests he could carry out with the small sample showed that it was unlike any other metal he knew. Back he went to Forster's store and bought the whole supply. It was not much, about 1½ grams (there are 28 grams to the ounce) and the price was high; Forster charged 21 shillings.

Probably angry with himself for having spent so much money, all the dark suspicions that Chevenix had had in the beginning returned and he went on record saying that the "new metal" was only a mixture of platinum and mercury; he even went so far as to say that he had duplicated it.

Nothing is easier than to make an amalgam (that is, a mixture of mercury and some other metal); therefore other chemists could test the claim in just a quarter hour of their spare time. They always obtained a soft amalgam, never a hard metal. When the truth—that it was really a new metal—

became known, Chevenix was so depressed by his hastiness that he swore he would never perform a chemical experiment again. As far as we know, he kept his word.

Though Chevenix had been mistaken in thinking that the new metal was an amalgam of platinum, there really was a connection with platinum. This metal, as has been mentioned, is found in nuggets as gold is,[8] but, also like gold, it occurs as dust, mixed in with sand. Such sands are logically known as "platinum sands," but they contain other metals too, gold dust and, often, lead in tiny globules. The French chemist, H. V. Collett-Descotil, was the first to suspect, in 1803, that the platinum sands might contain more metals than just platinum, gold and lead. He noticed that some "platinum" from the platinum sands developed a blue sheen when hot, something platinum doesn't do. And a platinum compound that is normally yellow was sometimes reddish. He suspected that both changes were due to the presence of an unknown metallic element.

In that suspicion he was wrong, for there were *two* unknown metals present.

For some reason Collett-Descotil did not concentrate on the suspected new elements so that credit for their discovery goes to Dr. William Hyde Wollaston (1766–1828), the son of an English clergyman. The new metal which acquires a blue sheen when hot, was named "palladium," but Wollaston did not release the news until after he had also discovered the second element. It was the one that is known as "rhodium." To obtain these new metals—especially rhodium—a fairly complicated series of operations had to be carried out, but Dr. Wollaston was famous for excellent eyesight and very steady hands. Because of his habit of not saying anything unless he was certain of his facts, his friends nick-

[8] The largest platinum nugget known is in the Demidoff Museum in Leningrad. It weighs 17⅓ pounds and was found in the northern Urals.

named him The Pope and one Dr. Marcet wrote to Berzelius in Sweden: "The dear Doctor, pope that he is, has taken seriously to hunting and already acquits himself with much success. The fact is he does not know how to do anything poorly."

Because the two new metals were associated with platinum and resembled it chemically, it became customary at an early date to call them the "platinum metals." Two more such metals were announced during the same year (1804). They were iridium and osmium and their discoverer, Smithson Tennant (1761–1815) was, like Wollaston, the son of a clergyman. He studied under Joseph Black, acquired a medical doctorate but never practiced medicine. For some time Wollaston had been his assistant, but by the time both of them tackled the platinum sands they were working independently.

Nor were they the only ones working in this restricted field. The French chemist, Nicolas-Louis Vauquelin, as well as his pupil, Collett-Descotil, also investigated platinum sands. They worked separately, too, and both reported that certain compounds had an unpleasant odor, "like concentrated onions," as one of them put it. But they failed to isolate the metal that produced these smelly compounds (osmium) and they either overlooked or disregarded the evidence for still another platinum metal. Tennant isolated both so that, counting platinum itself, five platinum metals were known by the end of 1804. We now know that there are six.

The sixth was not definitely discovered until 1845 and it was only proper that it was discovered in Russia, the country that produced most of the platinum available at the time. The first to suspect its existence was not a Russian, however, but a German working in Russia. His name was Gottfried Wilhelm Osann (1796–1866), who was born in Weimar as the son of a local government official. After obtaining his doctorate, he first taught physics and chemistry at the University of Erlangen. In 1823 he accepted a professorship at the University of Dorpat. There was no language problem because 90 percent of all the courses taught at Dorpat were taught in German. In fact, the University of Dorpat considered itself a German university located in Russia.[9]

While Osann was at Dorpat, where he taught for five years, the Russian government began preparations for the first issue of platinum coins and chemists became interested in platinum sands once more. In the course of his investigations, Osann found that one of his solutions produced crystals that certainly were not compounds of a known element. Osann tried to isolate the new element, but while he was not successful, it seemed to him that more than one new element was involved, probably three. He was a bit hasty and gave them names even before he had discovered them. The first one he named "ruthenium" (after an old name for Russia), the second "polinium" (from Greek *polios,* meaning "gray"), and the third "pluranium" (from *pl*atinum and *Ur*al mountains). He returned to Germany in 1829 and soon afterward admitted that his discovery had been a mistake.

The actual discoverer of the sixth platinum metal was a Baltic Russian, a native of Dorpat, with the delightful name of Karl Karlovitch Klaus (1796–1864). Klaus, the son of a portrait painter, first became an apothecary's apprentice, then had his own pharmacy, then became professor of chemistry at Kazan and acquired professional fame for finding new methods of separating the platinum metals. But he also wrote many articles (both in Russian and in German) about the plants of the Volga steppes, culminating in a large book that is usually referred to as *Volga Flora.*

In about 1842 Klaus began to wonder about Osann's ex-

[9] Dorpat is now called Tartu and is the capital of the Estonian province of the same name.

periments and failure and reasoned that Osann might have been successful if he had had more material for chemical analysis. By that time the platinum coins were issued in quantity and that meant that the platinum refinery in St. Petersburg should have large amounts of "residue," material left over after the platinum had been extracted. Klaus applied to the official in charge of the refinery and was given 20 pounds of the "useless" residue. Within a few years Klaus had isolated the metal that had eluded Osann. How much work this involved is shown by the fact that Klaus wrote 17 separate reports about it. They were all published in the *Bulletin of the Academy of Science* in St. Petersburg.

Because the metal had come from Russian mines and the work had been supported, at least in part, by the Russian government, Klaus named it "ruthenium," the "Russian metal."

At that point Osann, from his home in Germany, suddenly made himself heard and insisted that Klaus had only isolated the metal pluranium that he had discovered a dozen years earlier. Klaus wrote a long and careful paper showing that the metal Osann had suspected and the one he, Karl Karlovitch Klaus, had isolated could not possibly be the same. Osann may have grumbled in private but soon kept quiet publicly and that finished the case.

VI. MORE NEW METALS

After the time of Scheele, Bergman, Lavoisier and Klaproth, chemistry was dominated for decades by four other men, all mentioned earlier. They were Davy in England, Berzelius in Sweden, St. Claire Deville in France and Wöhler in Germany. Among them they usually succeeded where the earlier generation of chemists had failed. In part this was due to the fact that they had a new tool, the electric current.

Davy was born on December 17, 1778, in Penzance, Cornwall and christened Humphry. At the age of thirty-three he became Sir Humphry Davy; it so happened that he was knighted on the day before his wedding. As a boy Davy had several hobbies that stayed with him all his life. They were storytelling (he became an excellent lecturer later), mineral collecting, fishing and translating Latin poems into English verse. At seventeen he was apprenticed to the apothecary, Borlase, in Penzance and decided that he would use his spare time to study all the sciences, one after the other. In 1796 he began with mathematics, in 1797 chemistry followed and then came four years of medical studies. In 1801 he was appointed professor of chemistry at the Royal Institution and in 1802 he became interested in electricity.

In that, he had been beaten by another Englishman, the Londoner William Nicholson (1753–1815). Count Alessandro Volta had built his first current-generating battery in 1800, which consisted of pieces of copper and zinc in salty water. Later, Volta simplified his arrangement by using pairs of copper and zinc plates that were separated by cardboard (and sometimes felt) disks soaked in salt water. Since such a "voltaic pile," as it was called, is easy to build; Nicholson had only to read a description to duplicate the invention. Experiments with the pile very quickly led to the discovery that water could be decomposed into hydrogen and oxygen by the current.

Davy heard Volta lecture in Paris and decided on having such a battery in his own laboratory; since the electric current could decompose water, which could not be done by any other known method, it might decompose other substances, too. He probably started out with small voltaic piles but later he had batteries built that were the largest of their time, and possibly the largest ever. One set consisted of 100 pairs of square copper and zinc plates, each measuring six by six inches; another set was made of 150 plate pairs measuring four by four inches. The two could be used in conjunction with each other.

For his first experiments, Davy used an "alkali" that had defied Lavoisier's attempts to decompose it. Only a century before Lavoisier, the substance, called "niter," "neter," "natron" and other similar names, was a general term for two different substances. As late as 1758 the German chemist, Andreas Sigismund Marggraf, pointed out that there had to be a difference. If you had a fire with a flame that was not too strongly luminous itself, one kind of "alkali" colored the flame yellow, while the other kind colored it reddish-violet. Klaproth had then suggested that the "alkali" from plant ashes be called "kali" and the other "alkali," which was found in the ground, be called "natron." Lavoisier readily accepted the fact that there was a difference. He did not use the same terms, and he was chemically helpless with both.

Humphry Davy used the type that Klaproth had called "kali"; he dissolved it in water and then used his battery on the solution. But the current only decomposed the water into hydrogen and oxygen, although the water, while the current was on, behaved in a strange manner; it looked as if it were boiling violently. Davy then tried the current on the dry substance, without any success at all. We now know that the dry potash (for that is what the kali was) simply does not conduct an electric current and is, therefore, not influenced by it.

Success came when he used dry potash on a platinum disk and exposed it to the air for a short time so that its surface became moist enough to conduct the current. The platinum disk was connected to the negative wire from the battery, Davy held the positive wire, also made of platinum, and touched it to the top of the piece of potash. He reported:

> A vivid action was soon observed to take place. The potash began to fuse at both its points of electrization. There was a violent effervescence at the upper surface; at the lower, or negative, surface, there was no liberation of elastic fluid [gas]; but small globules . . . similar to quicksilver appeared, some of which burnt with explosion and bright flame

> as soon as they were formed, and others remained and were merely tarnished, and finally covered by a white film which formed on their surfaces.

Because he had started with potash, Davy called the new metal "potassium"; a few days later he repeated the experiment using soda instead of potash and isolated another new element: sodium.

The scientific world was amazed, but Davy had some surprising reactions. A visitor to his laboratory, picking up a few freshly formed beads of potassium, exclaimed: "Bless me, isn't it heavy!" Actually potassium weighs less than water, but since it was a metal the visitor was convinced that it had to be heavy. A few chemists cautioned Davy not to be hasty in his announcements. It was possible, they said, that he had made a mistake. Ammonia plus hydrogen produce ammonium, they said; maybe Davy's potassium was a compound of potash plus hydrogen. But Davy showed that hydrogen could not be liberated from potassium, hence it had to be a metal and therefore an element.

Of course, Davy went on, if the electric current had worked wonders twice, it could be expected to do so again. Davy was right, but there was a short delay. The next element he tackled was the one known as "calcium," the metal in limestone, of which whole mountain ranges are composed.

By that time Davy's larger battery was at the point of running down because, naturally, every experiment had been repeated many times. The members of the Royal Society were determined to keep Davy working and bought him a new battery. It consisted of 2,000 plate pairs housed in 200 electrically connected containers, each plate measuring about 5¾ by 5¾ inches. With the help of this new battery Davy tried to decompose lime, but without success. He observed what seemed to be some decomposition in the moist lime, but could not find any new metal. Then he tried another approach.

If his reasoning was correct, lime was an oxide of an unknown metal. Producing the metal meant separating it from the oxygen. His newly found potassium combined easily with oxygen; maybe the potassium would "steal" the oxygen from the unknown metal, with a little push by the electric current. If Davy had tried to do this using a closed vessel from which the air had been evacuated, it might have worked; as it was done, it did not. Davy thought that he failed because he could not raise the temperature high enough. Next he mixed dry lime with potash and fused the mixture, covered it with naphtha and applied the current. This time he could see droplets of metal appear, but they burst into flame, oxidizing so that, when it was all over, he again had the mixture of potash and lime with which he had started out.

Berzelius enters the story at this point so perhaps this is the right moment to introduce him formally. Jöns Jakob Berzelius—he was not made a baron until late in life—was born in 1779 at Westerlösa, Sweden, where his father was the school principal. Young Berzelius was not a good pupil, but entered the University of Upsala to study medicine in 1797 and was appointed, two years later, "physician to the poor" in Medevi. At that time he became interested in chemistry and read everything he could find about it. Of course, he heard about Volta's pile and built his own, consisting of the largest size of Swedish copper coins, with zinc disks of matching size that he had cast himself. By 1806 he became lecturer in chemistry at the war academy and soon met Dr. M. M. af Pontin, the King's personal physician, who was also interested in chemistry.

Of course, the two knew about Davy's work with potassium and sodium and, like Davy, they tried to extend the investigation to lime. Meanwhile Davy had had the idea of mixing lime with the oxide of mercury, hoping to drive off all the oxygen and obtain an amalgam of the new metal and mercury. Unless the new metal happened to have a very low melting point, it should be simple to distil the mercury out of the amalgam, leaving the unknown metal behind. But Davy had never obtained enough amalgam to be useful. Berzelius and Dr. Pontin, presumably after a number of failures, had had the same idea and Berzelius wrote to Davy that they, with a somewhat different procedure, had obtained barium amalgam and even an amalgam with the metal in lime.

Following the suggestion of the two Swedish scientists—to whom he gave full credit—Davy mixed moist lime with mercury oxide, then hollowed out a small depression in the center of the mixture, filled it with liquid mercury and touched his wire to the mercury. This time he obtained enough amalgam to carry out his original idea: the mercury was boiled out of the amalgam and calcium metal was left behind. However, it was not pure; really pure calcium was finally obtained by the French chemist Moissan around the year 1900.

Davy's next success was to obtain barium metal.

The one after that was the isolation of strontium.

Then came lithium, which had been discovered by Berzelius' friend, Johan August Arfvedson (1752–1841), while working in Berzelius' laboratory. Since the lithium compound that Arfvedson isolated came from pulverized rock, while potassium came from vegetable matter, Arfvedson called it "lithium" (from Greek *lithos*, meaning "stone"). He made his discovery late in 1817 or early in 1818; a few months later, Davy obtained a small amount of lithium metal by his method. Arfvedson's skill as a chemical analyst was highly praised by everybody who knew him—but Arfvedson disappointed them all by buying, in 1820, an iron forge and a large tract of land and living the life of a manufacturer and landowner.

The long list of Sir Humphry Davy's successes does not mean that he was invariably successful with everything he tried. He tried unsuccessfully to decompose zirconia in order to obtain the metal zirconium. He was convinced that silica was not an element as some others thought, but, though he was right, he failed to obtain the element silicon. He was also convinced that nitrogen was not an element and spent some time in 1808 and 1809 trying to decompose it. He failed, for nitrogen *is* an element.

But the isolation of magnesium was another triumph.

Like calcium compounds, magnesium compounds are not rare. The famous Dolomite Mountains in the Alps that seem to glow with a light of their own at sunset consist of a mixture of calcium carbonate and magnesium carbonate. The latter mineral, in fairly pure condition, was sold in Italy under the name of "magnesia alba" for medicinal purposes in the eighteenth century. That magnesia was not the same as lime was realized by Joseph Black in 1755; he published a small and famous book with the title: *Experiments upon Magnesia Alba, Quicklime and Some Other Alkaline Substances.* The German Marggraf made the same discovery four years later without knowing about Black's treatise—at that time English was not yet taught much in continental Europe. Davy was the first to make magnesium amalgam and then magnesium metal from the amalgam. He suggested the name of "magnium" so that it would not be confused with manganese, but everybody else thought that the metal from magnesia should be called "magnesium," even at the risk that nonchemists might think it was magnetic.

Somewhat larger amounts of magnesium were obtained

through a different process in 1830 by Antoine-Alexandre B. Bussy in Paris. Nowadays magnesium is one of the metals that are produced in quantity, mainly from minerals associated with rock salt. But magnesium was also the first metal that was extracted from sea water in large quantities.

Some time during the Middle Ages a white salt was imported into Europe from Tibet, possibly by Venetian merchants. The trade name was "tinkal," probably the Tibetan name for it. By the sixteenth century "tinkal" was called by the name it still bears, namely "borax," and it was stated that it was very useful in soldering. At about the same time the substance now known as "boracic acid" was made in Germany and Torbern Bergman satisfied himself that it actually was a true acid. Davy, it goes without saying, tried to decompose it, but the electric treatment produced only a thin layer of an olive-brown color. He then tried a purely chemical method, heating boracic acid with metallic potassium in a gold vessel, again obtaining a brown substance. He named it "boracium."

At the same time, two Frenchmen had been after the suspected new element, too. They were Joseph Louis Gay-Lussac (1778–1850), who also acquired fame as a balloonist, and Louis Jacques Thenard[1] (1777–1857), both professors of chemistry in Paris. While they were thinking about the problem, news of Humphry Davy's successes reached the ears of Emperor Napoleon. Napoleon did two things: he awarded Davy a prize of 2,500 francs, even though France was at war with England at the time, and he ordered a large voltaic battery to be built for Gay-Lussac and Thenard. But before the battery was ready, the two chemists had found a purely chemical method of obtaining the metal: they heated boracic

[1] Many books spell the name Thénard, but Thenard himself never used the accent.

acid and potassium in a copper tube! They suggested that the element be called "bore." Several decades later Wöhler in Germany as well as Sainte-Claire Deville in France obtained boron in somewhat purer form; really pure boron was prepared for the first time in 1909 by Dr. E. Weintraub of the General Electric Company.

Iodine is another of the elements discovered during this fruitful period. Its discoverer was the Frenchman, Bernard Courtois (1777–1838), born in Dijon. His father, Jean Baptist Courtois was a wine merchant who later added the manufacture of vinegar and the production of saltpeter to his enterprises. At that time the large deposits of saltpeter in South America were still unknown and it had to be extracted from seaweed. The process was to dry the seaweed, burn it in ditches, shovel the ashes into large pots, add water and boil them. The process of obtaining saltpeter from seaweed ashes was, naturally, called "saltpeter boiling" and the practitioners were called "saltpeter boilers." The whole procedure was possible only because seaweed has the peculiarity of accumulating chemicals that are dissolved in sea water. Therefore, the "mother liquor," as the result of the first boiling of the ashes was called, was a collection of a large number of chemicals,[2] of which only the compounds of sodium and of potassium (that is, salt and saltpeter as far as the saltpeter boilers cared) were of interest.

As the mother liquor was boiled, sodium chloride (salt) first appeared as a precipitate at the bottom of the pot. Then the liquid was poured into another pot and boiled some more. (Meanwhile, the precipitate from the first pot was dissolved in water again and purified by more boiling.) The second boil-

[2] Compounds of the metals potassium, sodium, calcium and magnesium with each of the following: chlorine, bromine, carbon, sulphur and the still to be discovered iodine.

ing of the mother liquor then produced potassium chloride and potassium sulphate. The remaining liquid, transferred to still another pot, still contained the same collection of chemicals as the original mother liquor, but in different proportions. Since most of the salt and the saltpeter had been removed, there was now a higher concentration of potassium iodide and sodium iodide in the liquid, but also many sulphur compounds which were customarily destroyed by adding sulphuric acid.

Courtois, one day in 1811, made a mistake; he added too much. The result was a cloud of violet vapor, beautiful in appearance but irritating in odor. The vapors condensed on nearby surfaces that were cool. But the vapor did not condense into a liquid as one would normally expect, but formed dark shiny crystals. Courtois carried out a number of experiments and found that the new substance could not be decomposed by heat, that it combined readily with phosphorus, with hydrogen and with some metals, and that it was reluctant to combine with carbon and oxygen. All of this looked as if he had discovered a new element, but he had to stop there. He could not afford to spend much time in further investigations and he did not own a well-equipped chemical laboratory. He asked his friends, Charles-Bernard Desormes and Nicolas Clément (who later became Desormes' son-in-law), to finish the investigation, and they soon announced the discovery of the new substance, stating that Courtois was the original discoverer.

Clément felt sure that this was a new element, but he lacked final proof. He gave samples to several French chemists and to Sir Humphry Davy. Both Davy and Gay-Lussac published their investigations, which proved the elementary nature of the substance, which received the name of "iodine," and in 1820 one Dr. Coindet of Geneva introduced it into medical practice.

After 1814 Humphry Davy abandoned his hunt for new elements and became interested in other subjects. His invention of a safety lamp for miners brought him more acclaim than any of his earlier discoveries. Explosions of gases that had accumulated in coal mines still happened, but far less often than they had when the miners had had to use open lamps. The invention consisted of enclosing the flame in wire gauze through which the gases could not penetrate, but atmospheric oxygen could, so that the lamp kept burning without igniting the coal gases. The owner of British mines thanked Davy by presenting him with table silver worth 2,500 pounds, and the Czar of all the Russias sent him an enormous gold-plated vase of solid silver. The King of England made him a baronet and the Royal Society elected him president seven consecutive times.

Davy died on May 29, 1829, in Geneva.

Jöns Jakob Berzelius was Sweden's leading chemist and the author of the most complete and competent chemistry handbooks of his time. But if he was not Sweden's worst businessman of the period, he came close to it, for his commercial ventures usually did not work out.

In 1810 he became a partner in a vinegar factory that subsequently went bankrupt, and Berzelius found himself 1,000 Riksdalers in debt, which took him ten years to pay off. In 1816 he bought, with his friends Gahn and Eggertz, a sulphuric acid factory near Gripsholm. Gahn died soon and Berzelius, who was busy as a professor and chief of a laboratory, was the only scientist in that factory. In 1826 it burned down and all that Berzelius could recover was his original investment.

But the purchase of the sulphuric acid factory had a scientific result. Sulphuric acid was made in large containers of metallic lead and Berzelius expected to see a muddy deposit (mainly sulphur) at the bottom. He did not expect the mud to look reddish. The color could be the result of either the presence of iron or of arsenic. Berzelius tested the mud for these two elements, but they were absent. Berzelius treated the mud with acid and obtained a precipitate that looked white but turned gray after being subjected to a sharp flame. If the flame was turned on the gray matter, a penetrating smell of rotten cabbage developed. Berzelius later found out that the burning of a single grain was enough to make a large room uninhabitable for hours.

At this moment Berzelius remembered two things which, unfortunately, contradicted each other. His correspondent, Klaproth, had complained about the smell when he was working on tellurium. On the other hand his friend, Gahn, had been unable to discover tellurium in the ores which they used.[3] After treating the mud with *aqua regis* and sulphuric acid, he had a powder of a deep yellow color. He mixed this with potassium and heated it, and after the reaction had taken place, he tried to dissolve what was left in water. Only a part dissolved, resulting in an orange-colored liquid. After some time reddish flakes appeared; when Berzelius added nitric acid, they increased in number and size.

Because of Klaproth's report, Berzelius repeated the experiment with tellurium and found the following differences:

	Tellurium	*The new element (selenium)*
color of precipitate	gray	red
colored flame of burning paper	green	bright blue
smell	none	penetrating

[3] Since tellurium does not cause such a smell, Klaproth's minerals must have contained a small percentage of selenium, the element Berzelius was about to discover.

After a number of additional experiments Berzelius was convinced that he had a new element which was often associated with tellurium. Since tellurium has its name from Latin *tellus,* for "earth," Berzelius took the Greek word *selēnē,* for "moon," and called it "selenium." Although associated with tellurium, selenium resembles sulphur in its chemical reactions and even somewhat in its appearance, except that it is gray. Selenium also exists in a glassy form.

The first people to discover a practical use for selenium were the glassmakers. They found that it was even better than manganese for removing unwanted color from glass. Much later, in 1873, William Smith made a very surprising discovery. Working with the gray "metallic" form of selenium, he found that it was a very poor conductor of an electric current in the dark, but a good one when a light shone upon it. The result of this discovery was the first photoelectric cell, and in 1880 Alexander Graham Bell demonstrated his "photophone," the transmission of sound over a light beam with the aid of selenium cells.

The next element to be discovered by Berzelius was thorium and the name was derived from that of the Norse god, Thor. In 1815, before he had discovered selenium, Berzelius thought that he had found a new element, and he named it "thorium." Ten years later he realized that he had made a mistake, and the "new element" was just yttrium phosphate. But in 1829 he did find a new element, and he named it "thorium" again. This time there was no mistake. It came from a mineral that had been found in Norway and looked like gadolinite, the ore of tantalum. The mineral is now called "thorite"; it is thorium silicate.

Thorium is one of the elements that are hard to isolate in pure form, but Berzelius obtained thorium metal that, while impure, was pure enough to determine most of its characteristics. Virtually pure thorium was not obtained until 1914, when Doctors D. Lely and L. Hamburger, working in Germany, distilled a mixture of thorium chloride and sodium in an evacuated steel cylinder at a high temperature.

One of the characteristics of thorium that Berzelius could not discover was found independently by two researchers in 1898. They were Madame Marie Curie in Paris and Professor Gerhardt Carl Schmidt of the University of Münster, who both found that thorium is naturally radioactive.

Though Berzelius discovered several elements himself and helped in the discovery of a few others, his main contributions to chemistry were of a more theoretical nature, although based on an incredible amount of laboratory work. He published a list of the atomic weights of the 43 elements known in his lifetime. In this list the weight of oxygen is assigned the value of 100 and all others are listed accordingly. During the same year that this list was published, he published a list of the composition of 2,000 different chemical compounds, and he also invented the system of chemical notation that is still in use. After this last achievement, Berzelius was badly in need of relaxation and so he made a trip to Paris with the Swedish count, Löwenhjelm. He spent his time with some of the most prominent scientists of the day, Gay-Lussac, Thenard, Vauquelin and Alexander von Humboldt. A few years later, during a trip to Germany, he not only met several of his former pupils, but also had a long discussion with Johann Wolfgang von Goethe.

In 1829 he was decorated with the Great Cross of the Order of Gustaf Vasa, and when he married, in 1835, the King of Sweden sent him a wedding present that was read prior to the ceremony, a letter written in French which made him Baron Berzelius. Berzelius died August 7, 1848.

The next element to be mentioned here is one of the

lightest and most abundant in the earth's crust; today, it is one of the cheapest and, after iron, the most useful: aluminum.

As in the cases of calcium, sodium and so forth, aluminum compounds have been known since antiquity. The Romans knew that the substance now called "alum" was useful in medicine, that it helped in the dyeing of wool, and they even knew that it could be used for fireproofing combustible materials. They also knew two other aluminum compounds although they did not even guess that they were related to alum: the gemstones ruby and sapphire.

One of the early investigators of alum was Andreas Sigismund Marggraf (1709–1782), who was born in Berlin and lived there most of his long life. He was a disciple of Stahl of the phlogiston theory but that did not prevent him from becoming a pioneer in chemical analysis. If he had been born only half a century later, he might have become a serious competitor to Klaproth or Berzelius. It was Marggraf who distinguished sodium salts from potassium salts by their coloring effects on flames; it was Marggraf who had investigated magnesia and it was Marggraf again who proved that alum, or alumina, was a distinct "earth" that differed from all others then known. But that was as far as he could go with the scientific tools then available to him.

More than a century later Sir Humphry Davy used his big battery on alumina, but he failed to isolate the element. Even his largest battery was still far too small for this purpose. Electric current of the power that can only be produced by dynamos (invented by Davy's assistant and pupil, Michael Faraday, who has often been called Davy's most important discovery) is required to make aluminum metal.

The metal really has two discoverers. They were contemporaries, one, a Dane, the other, a German. In addition to being contemporaries, they had a number of other things in common. Both men held medical doctorates that they did not use, both were chemists and both derive their main fame from other discoveries, not from aluminum.

They were Hans Christian Oersted (1777–1851) and Friedrich Wöhler (1800–1882). Oersted was born on the Danish island of Langeland, the son of an apothecary, whose helper he became at the age of twelve. Learning whenever and whatever he could, he succeeded in passing the examination that permitted him to attend the University of Copenhagen. In 1799 he received his medical doctorate, but began to lecture on chemistry and physics, which he had also studied, and he became professor of physics at the university in 1806.

Oersted was very much interested in electricity, and in the course of his experiments he discovered that there is a close relationship between magnetism and electricity. Simplifying things a little, one might say that he discovered the electromagnet. That is what made him famous. His chemical discovery was made earlier, when he was relatively unknown, and he published the results of his experiments with aluminum in a small Danish journal which was hardly read outside his homeland. For this reason the very fact that he was the codiscoverer of aluminum remained unknown for almost a century. Some time in 1823 Oersted took aluminum chloride and heated it with potassium amalgam, obtaining aluminum amalgam and potassium chloride. He then distilled the amalgam in such a manner that the atmosphere was kept out, and the result was a lump of (impure) aluminum. In 1919 several Danish scientists repeated the experiment, proving that aluminum could be obtained by that method.

The other, and definite, discoverer of aluminum was the German, Friedrich Wöhler. Born near Frankfurt am Main, Wöhler was a brilliant student at the university after having been, at best, an average student in high school. Although he took his medical doctorate, his professor in chemistry, Leopold Gmelin, advised him to devote all his time to chemistry. Wöhler then decided to study with Berzelius and wrote to him; Berzelius replied that a student of Gmelin could hardly learn anything from him, but ended his letter with the words: "You may come, if you wish." Wöhler did go to Sweden and the two men became lifelong friends.

In 1825 Wöhler joined the faculty of the University of Berlin and was appointed full professor three years later. The discovery for which Wöhler is mainly famous was the synthesizing of a substance called "urea." Up to that moment urea was known only as the product of living bodies (of men and animals) and it was believed that only organisms, because of the "life force" inherent in them, could produce such compounds, which were, therefore, called "organic compounds." Wöhler produced such an "organic compound," using only materials that were not of organic origin—and "life force" joined phlogiston as a figment of the imagination.

It is true that we still distinguish between "inorganic" and "organic" chemistry, but only as a method of classification. As a matter of fact, many so-called organic compounds in commercial or medicinal use that were first extracted from plants or from the glands of animals are now made in the laboratory—insulin for the treatment of diabetes being the most recent example.

The process for obtaining aluminum metal which Wöhler had reasoned out, required a number of steps and the final step could be expected to generate a great amount of heat. Wöhler used a platinum crucible for this final step. But then he found that his aluminum was contaminated not only with leftover potassium, but with platinum as well. He repeated his experiments in porcelain crucibles and obtained aluminum in the form of a gray powder; he did not succeed in melting this powder into a metal until 1845. But he was the first to describe all the characteristics of metallic aluminum.

The first to prepare virtually pure aluminum was the French chemist, Henri Sainte-Claire Deville (1818–1881). He studied in Paris, then became professor of chemistry at the University of Besançon, but was soon called to Paris. While teaching in Paris, he became curious about aluminum and followed Wöhler's method, except that he substituted sodium for potassium. The reason for this substitution is unknown, but sodium produced better results, and Deville was able to obtain large globules of the metal. Napoleon III heard about this and, since the first Napoleon had supported his chemists, Napoleon III did not have to think long: he would support the French chemists of his time.

Generously supplied with both funds and official encouragement, Sainte-Claire Deville went to work. Some of the first aluminum he produced was made into table cutlery for Napoleon III, who, while eating his food with the aid of the exotic metal, dreamed of the day when all French cavalry would wear aluminum armor. His favorite chemist, in the meantime, had other worries, though his dreams may have been the same. His process of obtaining aluminum needed sodium metal, which was expensive, costing about 200 dollars a pound in 1855. Potassium was slightly cheaper, but since sodium is more abundant in nature, Sainte-Claire Deville reasoned that it should be possible to make sodium cheap. That he was both correct and successful is shown by the fact that the price of sodium was down to two dollars per pound in 1890. When he began to produce aluminum in fair amounts, several of his compatriots began to drop hints. After all Wöhler's aluminum had been impure; he had said so himself. Monsieur Sainte-Claire Deville's aluminum was practically pure and he had every reason to consider himself the true discoverer of aluminum. His answer was simple: he cast a large aluminum medal with the inscription

WÖHLER 1827

and sent it to Wöhler.

But while he produced fair amounts of the metal, it was still rather expensive, costing a few dollars per pound. An American, Charles Martin Hall (1863–1914), when still a student at Oberlin College, decided that he would find a way of making *cheap* aluminum. In February 1886 he succeeded, having used electric current on *molten* (not dissolved) compounds of aluminum.[4] As so often happens, independent discoveries may be made at the same time, and a young French chemist, Dr. Paul-Louis Toussaint Hérault, found the same method two months or so after Hall.

The aluminum that could then be mass-produced by the Hall or Hérault process was fine for small objects and for teakettles and other kitchen utensils. But for engineering construction jobs like small boats, railroad cars and, later, airplanes, pure aluminum was too soft. The first really useful alloy for larger constructions was the one made in 1906 by the German metallurgist, Alfred Wilm. It contained 4 percent copper and 0.5 percent magnesium and was called "duralumin" or "Dural."

The next two stories about elements begin with mistakes.

Around the year 1815 a man named Roloff, who was the medical supervisor of the district in Germany of which the

[4] The first buttons of aluminum metal that Hall made are still preserved by the Aluminum Company of America and are jokingly referred to as "the crown jewels."

city of Magdeburg is the center, inspected the stocks of the pharmacies under his jurisdiction. One of the standard items on the pharmacies' shelves was zinc oxide, and when the supervisor (*Medizinalrat* or "medical councillor" was his official title) tested it with hydrogen sulphide, he obtained a yellow precipitate, a sure sign of the presence of poisonous arsenic. Roloff therefore ordered the whole supply confiscated. All the pharmacies had bought their zinc oxide from the same source, a chemical factory owned by a Mr. Bergmann in Silesia. Naturally Mr. Bergmann received a large number of angry letters, prompting him to carry out an analysis of the zinc oxide himself. He could not find any arsenic and sent a letter of protest to Roloff, enclosing samples of his analysis. He also sent samples to the supervisor of mines of his own district and to Friedrich Strohmeyer (1776–1835), professor of chemistry in Göttingen.

Now it so happened that Strohmeyer, who held a medical doctorate, performed the same function as Roloff in his own district and he too had noted an irregularity. His pharmacists had received zinc carbonate instead of zinc oxide. The factory that supplied the pharmacists happened to be not far away, so Strohmeyer went there to see what had occurred. The chief of the laboratory told him that he had supplied zinc oxide, but it had always looked yellowish instead of pure white and the pharmacists had rejected it, saying that it contained iron. While he had to admit the presence of the yellow color, the laboratory chief continued, he had not been able to find any iron in the oxide. So he had supplied zinc carbonate, which the apothecaries could convert into the oxide, if they wanted to, just by heating it.

Strohmeyer accepted the explanation; but this explanation covered only the commercial side of the problem. The scientific side had not been investigated carefully and he decided to do it himself. He took a quantity of the yellowish zinc oxide and treated it with acids in such a manner that the unknown substance (whatever it was that caused the yellow coloration) would be left behind in the form of its carbonate. Then he heated the carbonate to change it into an oxide.[5] The oxide was then heated in the presence of carbon, a simple reduction operation. A metal was left, as expected, and this metal had the interesting characteristic of being softer than lead when freshly isolated, but grew hard soon afterwards.

Strohmeyer had already finished his experiment when he received the samples from the dutiful supervisor, Roloff, and the outraged manufacturer, Bergmann. This enabled him to say that the new metal, which he called "cadmium," could be found in zinc ores from many places.

Roloff, who had already denounced Bergmann's zinc oxide as dangerous to the government of Prussia, grew doubtful when he saw Bergmann's analysis. He made one of his own and had to admit that there was no arsenic present. Then he heard about Strohmeyer's work and immediately claimed that he should be considered the discoverer of cadmium because he had seen the precipitate first. Bergmann retorted that, if Roloff did not acclaim Strohmeyer as the discoverer, the honor should go to him, because the element had been found in his products, but that that was a ridiculous claim, as ridiculous as Roloff's. Of course, Strohmeyer was the discoverer.

Industry found uses for cadmium quite soon. It was found that a chromium plating of iron and steel was improved if the iron was plated with cadmium first and the chromium applied on top of the cadmium. Another interesting use was

[5] The reasoning was that the heat would split the unknown element from the carbon, the carbon would combine with atmospheric oxygen and disappear, while more oxygen from the atmosphere would oxidize the element. This is precisely what happened.

in an alloy known as Wood's metal, consisting of 50 percent bismuth, 25 percent lead, 12.5 percent tin and 12.5 percent cadmium. This alloy melts at 70° centigrade (158° Fahrenheit); its melting point, therefore, is below the boiling point of water. It was used to plug open water pipes; in case of fire the plug melted easily and the water shot out of the pipe, an early kind of sprinkler system. During the First World War Wood's metal found an even more surprising use. Airplane designers needed fuel tanks that would fit into odd spaces. They had to have unusual shapes and sheet-metal workers did not know how to make them.

Then somebody had the idea of making the oddly shaped tanks out of solid castings of Wood's metal, electroplating them very heavily with copper and then melting out the Wood's metal by putting the whole into a vat of boiling water.

In a letter written in January 1831 to the German chemist, Justus von Liebig (1803–1873), the great Friedrich Wöhler said: "*Ich war ein Esel,*"—"I was an ass." The reason for this harsh self-criticism was the discovery of the element vanadium by somebody else. Berzelius had informed him about this in a letter written like a German fairy tale, which read, in part:

> High in the north there once lived the beautiful and lovable goddess Vanadis. One day there was a knock at her door, but the goddess remained seated, thinking that the visitor would knock again. But the one who had knocked went down the steps. The goddess was curious to see who had been so indifferent about her, went to the window and looked. Ah, she then said, that's the fellow Wöhler. Serves him right, if he had been a little more persistent I would have welcomed him.

To understand the banter one has to know the background. In 1801 Professor Andrés Manuel del Rio, born in Spain but living in Mexico, had examined a specimen of brown lead ore and had come to the conclusion that it contained a new metal, possibly similar to chromium. He named it "erythronium," from the Greek word for "red." Then he reconsidered; the ore seemed to consist only of lead oxide and chromic acid, but the presence of chromium in a lead ore was a discovery in itself, so he published a paper entitled: "Discovery of Chromium in the Brown Lead of Zimapán." Andrés Manuel del Rio had studied in Germany and had made friends with a fellow student, the young Baron Alexander von Humboldt. During a five-year trip to South America, from 1799 to 1804, von Humboldt met del Rio again and del Rio gave him a piece of the "brown lead of Zimapán." On returning to his native Berlin, von Humboldt gave it to Wöhler, with the information that del Rio had thought it contained a new element but that he had withdrawn his statement because Collett-Descotil had said it was merely impure chromium. Wöhler was sick at the time, having breathed some of the extremely poisonous fluoric acid in one of his experiments, and put the specimen aside.

In 1830 one of Berzelius' pupils, Nils Gabriel Sefström (1787–1854), who also held an unused medical doctorate, was confronted with a puzzle. An iron foundry at Ekersholm produced iron that was called "soft iron," a strange designation because it referred to iron that was especially tough and did not break easily. A Swedish mining chemist by the name of Rinmann had found a method of recognizing iron that was "soft" and that treatment of it with hydrochloric acid resulted in a black powder. But Sefström, experimenting with the especially "soft" iron from Ekersholm, also found the black powder. He analyzed it and found iron, silica, lime, copper, cobalt and a substance that showed some similarities to chromium. But the amount of the substance was so small that he had to give up testing it. But in the fall of the same year he could repeat his work with more material in Berzelius' laboratory. There was now no doubt that this was a new element and, since the original ore had come from the north, either Sefström or Berzelius thought of the goddess Vanadis and bestowed the name "vanadium."

Wöhler replied to Berzelius' banter in the same manner but there were signs, in addition to his letter to Justus von Liebig, that he was annoyed. He stated that Sefström's vanadium was identical with del Rio's erythronium and added that del Rio should be named the discoverer. But privately he repeatedly said: "The vanadium discovered by Sefström, or rather by Berzelius . . ."

Berzelius insisted that Sefström was the discoverer of the new element but it was he himself who investigated vanadium in fine detail. It so happens that vanadium can form very many compounds (with oxygen alone there are five different ones) and the work took several years. Even fifty years later chemists said that Berzelius' treatise on vanadium was so complete that, except for a correction of the atomic weight, nobody had been able to add anything of importance.

Berzelius knew that he had produced a thorough investigation but when someone complimented him on it he sighed: "I am now so tired of vanadium!"

To all these metals a new element that was not a metal was added in 1826. In that year the French pharmacist and chemist, Antoine Jérôme Balard (1802–1876), was busy hunting iodine. As has been said, iodine was discovered in ashes of seaweed and, since the iodine could hardly come from anywhere other than the sea, it had to have been dissolved in the water before the plants concentrated it. Balard tried to prove this assumption by finding iodine in sea water directly; as a side issue he wanted to see whether the seaweed of the

Mediterranean Sea, like the seaweed of the North Sea, also accumulated iodine.

Detecting the presence of iodine is simple; dissolved starch will turn blue even if only traces of iodine are present. Working with mother liquors from several places, Balard noticed one day that there was a yellowish layer above the layer of starch that had been colored by the iodine. The yellow layer not only had a different color; it also emitted a typical smell. Balard distilled the yellow portion and saw it turn into a thick red smoke that condensed into a liquid upon cooling. To purify whatever he had, he led the red smoke over a layer of calcium chloride, which would absorb any water that it might contain. The result was a few drops of a dark red liquid that evaporated easily and developed the typical strong smell.

In his report Balard stated that he had discovered a new element, and that it could be obtained in two ways. One consisted of adding chlorine to the mother liquor, then distilling it and capturing and condensing the red smoke. The other was to add chlorine to the mother liquor and then ether. Shaking the mixture produced a solution of the new element in the ether.

The French Academy assigned Gay-Lussac, Vauquelin and Thenard to check on Balard's work. They reported unanimously that Balard had indeed discovered a new element, and recommended that the Academy encourage the young chemist (it did; Balard became professor of chemistry at the Collège de France in Paris) but vetoed the name "muride" that he had proposed for the new substance. One member of the Academy suggested to Balard that "bromine" would be a better name, because of its pronounced and unpleasant smell (*bromos* is Greek for "stench") and Balard followed the suggestion.

If Balard had not discovered bromine in 1827, it would

have been discovered about a year later by the German, Carl Löwig (1803–1890), who, like Wöhler, was a pupil of Leopold Gmelin. Löwig had progressed to several compounds of bromine and was trying to obtain a larger quantity of them when Balard published his report. And if Löwig had failed, still another German, Justus von Liebig, a friend of Wöhler, and famous for his researches in organic and agricultural chemistry, might still have succeeded. A few years earlier a German industrial firm had asked him to analyze the contents of a bottle of mother-liquor residue and von Liebig "had seen quickly" that this was iodine chloride. When he read about Balard's discovery, he remembered the incident and a few minutes of testing proved to him that he had missed an element. The contents of the bottle yielded not quite 20 grams of bromine.

VII. LAW AND ORDER

In 1859, hundreds of well-known chemists all over Europe were invited to attend a Chemical Congress that would take place in the German city of Karlsruhe in the following year. Anyone could report on a new discovery, or on new procedures in analyzing minerals or other matters. But the main theme of the congress was a discussion on atomic and molecular weights and the valences of elements. When the congress opened, 140 chemists were present and the meetings planted the seed for a very important advance in chemistry—although it took nine years for the seed to ripen, sprout and bear fruit.

At the time of the congress about fifty chemical elements were known, although the list included a few, like fluorine, that were suspected to exist but had not yet been isolated. Many of the chemists present felt that their science was lacking something important, a system of classification. Other sciences, especially zoology and botany, already had such systems. A zoologist hardly needed more than one look at a newly discovered animal to know where it belonged in his system. If it was warm-blooded, with fur or traces of it, had a certain type of lungs and the organs for bearing live young, it was a mammal. If it was warm-blooded, had feathers and laid eggs, it was a bird. If it was egg-laying, had a changeable body temperature and a smooth or scaly skin without skin glands, it was a reptile. And so forth down the ladder to animals consisting of one cell only, like an amoeba.

Botanists had a similar list of characteristics which were used for classification. Physicists could classify the phenomena with which they were concerned and astronomers had a system that was several centuries old by that time. The chemists did not, or not yet.

A few beginnings had been made, though.

Johann Wolfgang Döbereiner (1780–1849), professor of chemistry at the University of Jena, had noticed some interesting relationships among elements in 1829. There were groups of elements that were quite similar in their chemical characteristics and also quite similar in their atomic weights. Iron (atomic weight 55.8), cobalt (at. wt. 58.9), and nickel (at. wt. 58.7) were all metals, all responded to a magnet, and all formed compounds that were chemically similar, although they might not look alike. A similar situation prevailed for osmium (at. wt. 190.2), iridium (at. wt. 192.2) and platinum (at. wt. 195.1). It was almost as if these two groups of elements were chemical triplets.

Döbereiner then discovered a different kind of triplets. The three metals, lithium, potassium, and sodium, also had many characteristics in common. Lithium has an atomic weight of 6.9 and potassium of 39.1. Adding these two atomic weights you obtained 46.0 and, halving this, you got 23, the atomic weight of sodium, which was the middle link in the trio. It also worked out for the three elements, chlorine, bromine and iodine. The atomic weight of chlorine is 35.5, that of iodine 127, which should give bromine an atomic weight of 81.2; in reality it is 80.[1] Then there was calcium (at. wt. 40), barium (at. wt. 137.4), and strontium in the middle with an atomic weight of 88.7, by Döbereiner's calculation; actually it is 87.6. Döbereiner called these groups of elements the "triads" and hoped that in time it would be found that all elements form such triads.

While Döbereiner's triads applied to less than half of the elements known, their existence proved that there was an order of some kind among them; the problem was to find it. The atomic weights must hold—and at the moment, hide—the clue or clues.

For the beginning of the thoughts about atoms we have to go back far beyond Döbereiner. The idea of atoms had been conceived long before Döbereiner had been born, in about 450 B.C. The father of the idea of atoms was the Greek philosopher, Demokritos,[2] who was born in a place called Abdera in Thrace in 470 B.C. and is said to have lived to the age of ninety.

Demokritos' reasoning was both simple and logical. He watched a fish swim in a pond and said to himself that this proved that water was not a continuous matter, for if it were, the fish could not force its body through it. But since it did, water had to consist of separate particles with spaces between

[1] In quoting these examples, I am using the modern atomic weights; in Döbereiner's time they were less precisely known so that his calculations worked out without discrepancies.

[2] Like Professor George Sarton, the great historian of science, I see no reason for writing the name "Democritus" in the Latin manner. The Greek letters clearly give the form "Demokritos" and, since we are no longer writing in Latin, there is no reason why the original form should not be preferred. The same applies to Epikuros of Samos, who will be mentioned soon.

them, so that the fish could push these particles aside. Reasoning about the wings of birds in the air and the growing roots of plants in the soil, he came to the conclusion that everything had to consist of separate particles. He summed up his thinking in the sentence: "Nothing exists except the atoms and empty space, everything else is just opinion." The only correction a modern scientist would make would be to say: "Atoms, radiation and empty space." Demokritos not only evolved the idea of atoms; he also provided the word. The ultimate particles of matter had to be so small that it was impossible to divide them farther; they were "indivisible," and in Greek this word is *atomos.*

Some forty years after the death of Demokritos, Epikuros (342?–270 B.C.) was born on the island of Samos. Later he moved to Athens, founded a school of philosophy and shocked everybody by admitting female students. Practically nothing of his writings has survived, but we do know that he embraced the atoms of Demokritos wholeheartedly. And his teachings, in turn, caused the Roman poet, Titus Lucretius Carus (95–55 B.C.) to join the atomists. He discussed them at length in the first book of his long poem, *De rerum natura* ("On the Nature of Things"), which was written around the year 60 B.C. It is quite possible that the examples he gave in the sample to follow were taken from the now lost works of Epikuros:

> Clothes hung up on the shore which waves break upon become moist, and then get dry if spread out in the sun. Yet it has not been seen in what way the moisture of the water has sunk into them, nor in what way this has been dispelled by heat. The moisture therefore is dispersed into small particles which the eyes are quite unable to see. After many years a ring on the finger is thinned on the underside by wearing, the drippings from an eave hollow a stone, the bent plowshare of iron imperceptibly decreases in the fields,

> and we behold the stone-paved streets worn down by the feet of the multitude. . . . Nature therefore works by unseen bodies.[3]

It may seem strange to us that these ideas, once pronounced, could vanish completely but it is not too difficult to understand why this happened. In the first place, the atomists had only advanced a reasonable idea; they had no way of proving it. Therefore, it was a philosophical opinion with which other philosophers might, or might not, agree. Added to this was the fact that nobody did anything for which the concept of atoms was needed. It did not help physicians in curing patients, nor it did help the metal workers, nor the weavers or dyers. Even the alchemists had no need for atoms.

The early chemists did, however, and the idea of the atom reappeared soon after modern chemistry began. The man who revived the concept, along with the word, was the English chemist, John Dalton (1766–1844). He first spoke of the need for thinking in terms of atoms in 1803 and then again, in a more thorough publication, in 1808. It sounds strange to us that other chemists of his period were not sure that "this Greek concept" was needed; Sir Humphry Davy, for example, was never completely convinced that atoms actually existed.

Before Dalton acquired fame by reviving "this Greek concept," he was famous for another investigation, and there is a little story that goes with it. The King of England wanted to see the famous scientist, who was ordered to present himself at court. For Dalton this was a problem, because he was a Quaker and a court presentation required the wearing of a colorful costume and a dress sword. He was obliged, as a Quaker, to wear dark, simple dress and no arms. But Dalton found a solution: over his Quaker dress he wore the long, wide and scarlet robe that he had worn while receiving his hon-

[3] From the prose translation of H. A. J. Munro (1864), who was a Fellow of Trinity College, Cambridge, England.

orary doctorate at Oxford. The robe hid the absence of the dress sword and, when fellow Quakers reproached him for having worn scarlet, he replied: "To thee it is scarlet, but not to me; it is green like the color of leaves." And he was not lying, for he was totally color blind. It was his investigation of color blindness that had brought him his first fame, and color blindness was called "Daltonism" for nearly a hundred years.

Before Dalton, Robert Boyle, one of the discoverers of phosphorus, and Sir Isaac Newton had both come to the conclusion that gases consisted of tiny and separate particles. Dalton extended the idea to liquids and solids, and his main argument was based on the "law of definite proportions," which had been stated a few years earlier, in 1799, by the French chemist, Joseph Louis Proust (1754–1826).

Proust had been making compounds under the most carefully controlled conditions and had found that the exact same proportion of elements always went into the making of a compound. For example, the production of copper carbonate required 5 parts of copper, 4 of oxygen and 1 of carbon, and the amounts used did not matter. One could use large amounts or small amounts, or amounts so small that they were hardly visible; the proportion of 5 to 4 to 1 remained unchanged. Well, said Dalton, this means that we can combine 5 atoms of copper with 4 atoms of oxygen and 1 atom of carbon. Or we can combine 5,000 atoms of copper with 4,000 atoms of oxygen and 1,000 atoms of carbon, and we then will obtain 1 "atom" (the term "molecule" had not yet been invented) of copper carbonate or 1,000 "atoms" of copper carbonate. It proved the existence of atoms, and it also indicated that the atoms of different elements could be compared with each other, for evidently an atom of carbon had a weight that differed from that of an atom of copper.

By comparing the proportions of the atoms in different

compounds, one could arrive at the weight of a single atom. Of course, this weight could not be expressed in ounces or grains or anything used in daily life. But one could determine that an atom of iron had to weigh more than 50 times as much as an atom of hydrogen. And that is just what Dalton did; he compared the weight of the atoms of other elements with the weight of the hydrogen atom. Naturally, a number of early mistakes were made. Dalton was not sure, for example, that the substance we now call "carbon dioxide" consisted of one atom of carbon and one of oxygen, or of one atom of carbon and two of oxygen. Others who came after Dalton—especially Berzelius—corrected the mistakes and refined the calculations.

Dalton made another valuable contribution: He introduced a system of chemical symbols. The alchemists had, of course, done this too, but mainly for the purpose of being mysterious. Torbern Bergman, in 1783, had also published a number of symbols (Figure 4) which he used in addition to the classical planetary symbols for the metals. His purpose had been to save space, and as can be seen, he also began to put symbols together to express compounds.

Dalton was as systematic about it as his knowledge per-

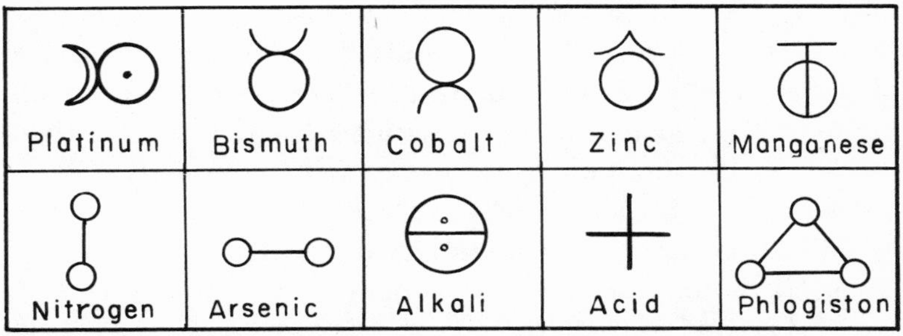

Platinum	Bismuth	Cobalt	Zinc	Manganese
Nitrogen	Arsenic	Alkali	Acid	Phlogiston

FIGURE 4. *Bergman's symbols for several then new elements and general concepts like acids and "phlogiston."*

mitted (see Figure 5). A circle with a dot in the center represented hydrogen, a circle without a dot represented oxygen, a circle with a cross inside represented sulphur. Since it was impossible to find a sufficiently large number of simple symbols, he used letters in his circles. A circle with an S inside meant silver, a circle with a *G* inside meant gold. But the important difference between Dalton's symbols and the old ones used by the alchemists was that the circle with the dot in it (which meant gold to the alchemists) now did not mean just "hydrogen"; it meant *an atom of hydrogen.* Other chemists reasoned that a system in which one set of elements was characterized by a symbol such as a circle divided into three or four parts, and another set characterized by letters inside circles, might cause confusion, so they started writing only letters, at first in circles and later without. And if they wanted to express a compound, such as carbon dioxide, they would write CO^2. But confusion was still possible, simply because different chemists spoke different languages. To a Frenchman the logical abbreviation for nitrogen was *A* (for *azote*), to a German it was *S* (*Stickstoff*); or where Dalton had used *G* (for gold), a Frenchman would prefer to use *O* (for *or*).

Jöns Jakob Berzelius established the present method. In the first place, he said, we have to agree on one language, and in order not to favor anyone, let us use Latin, which is neutral. And since there are more elements than there are letters in the alphabet, we cannot have single letters only; aluminum, antimony and arsenic all begin with an *A*, so let us write them *Al* and *As* for aluminum and arsenic, while antimony will get an *Sb* (for *stibium*). Finally, writing H^2O and CO^2 is misleading, too; somebody might think that the H should be squared or that CO has been squared. He suggested H_2O and CO_2, and this method is still followed. The Prussian Academy of Science was greatly impressed by (and in favor of) this new system. When Berzelius passed through Berlin,

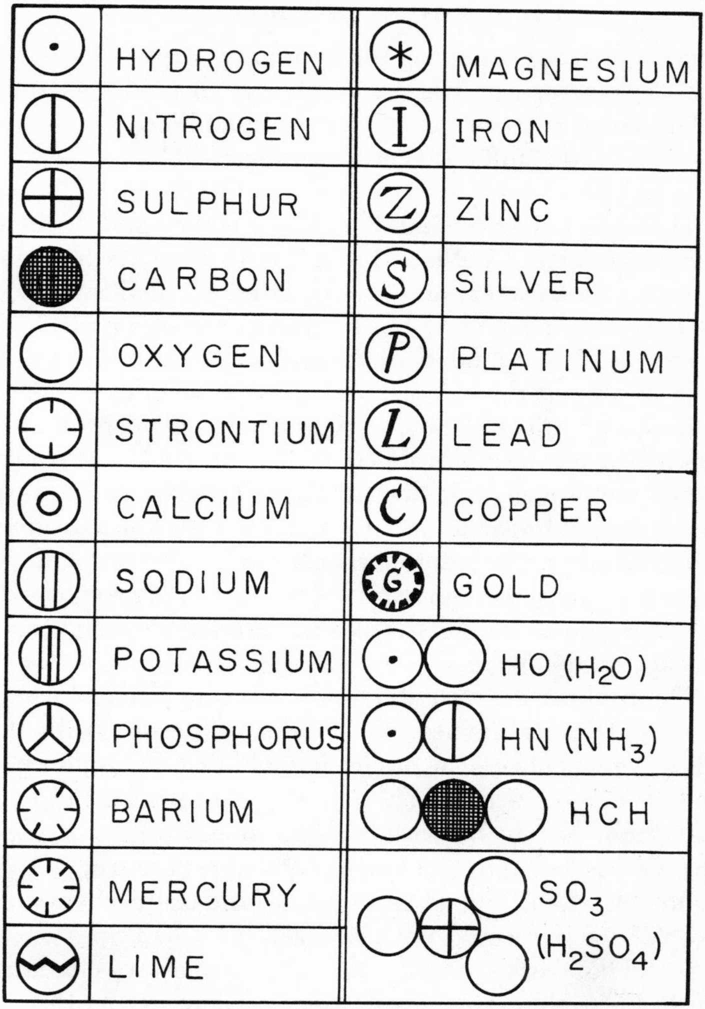

Symbol	Element	Symbol	Element
	HYDROGEN		MAGNESIUM
	NITROGEN	I	IRON
	SULPHUR	Z	ZINC
	CARBON	S	SILVER
	OXYGEN	P	PLATINUM
	STRONTIUM	L	LEAD
	CALCIUM	C	COPPER
	SODIUM	G	GOLD
	POTASSIUM		HO (H_2O)
	PHOSPHORUS		HN (NH_3)
	BARIUM		HCH
	MERCURY		SO_3 (H_2SO_4)
	LIME		

FIGURE 5. *Dalton's symbols for elements and a few simple compounds. What he pictured as HO meant water (H_2O); NH stands for NH_3, which is ammonia; HCH, which is methane, also called swamp gas; while SO_3 should be H_2SO_4, sulphuric acid. Note that the symbol for gold suggests a coin.*

they arranged a luncheon for him which took several hours because so many people wanted to say in public what Berzelius meant to them. He came out of that luncheon, to quote his own words, "full of soda water and praise."

The next man to be mentioned here is the English chemist and physiologist, William Prout (1785–1850), whose fame rests on one discovery and one hypothesis. The discovery was that the active agent in the human stomach is plain hydrochloric acid; it sounded unbelievable but it was true. The hypothesis was this: iron has an atomic weight of about 56, gold of 197, silver of 108, oxygen of 16, nitrogen of 14 and sulphur of 32; was it possible that there was only *one* element, namely hydrogen, and that all the other elements were just clusters of hydrogen atoms? He said so in 1815 and he himself found the thought so daring that his first publication about it was anonymous. He did know that some atomic weights were not whole numbers, but, he asked, were atomic weights actually known that well?

Those chemists who were not yet convinced of the existence of atoms brushed the whole matter aside, while those who were believers in atoms felt obliged to establish the atomic weights with far greater care. And it soon turned out that Prout had to be wrong. The atomic weight of copper always was found to be close to 63½ times the weight of the hydrogen atom, and chlorine also stubbornly always gave 35½. Since one could not very well have half an atom, the idea did not work. Actually, Prout had come very close to the truth, but only close, as we'll see in Chapter IX. But from 1815 to about 1910 it could only be concluded that Prout's hypothesis was totally incorrect.

This, then, was the background for the Chemical Congress of Karlsruhe. The assembled chemists discussed atomic weights, molecular weights, and valences. The latter term refers to the ability of an atom of one element to combine with atoms of other elements. Oxygen, for example, can hold two hydrogen atoms and so can zinc. Boron could hold three hydrogen atoms, while carbon could hold four. A difficulty with which the chemists still had to contend at the time is that some elements had three valences with some other elements, and five valences with another set of elements; antimony is an example of that. Chlorine looked even more capricious; it displayed, depending on the compound, one, three, five or seven valences. This, too, pointed to the need for a classification of some kind.

Several chemists who had attended the congress, plus a few who had only read about it, began to wonder in earnest about a classification and the first to publish such a system was the Frenchman, Alexandre E. Beguyer de Chancourtois (1820–1886) in 1862. Beguyer de Chancourtois was not primarily a chemist, but was professor of geology at the School of Mines in Paris. This helped to make his paper difficult for chemists to read, because he talked in geological terms. (That the editor of the scientific journal somehow neglected to publish his diagram was not his fault, but it made the report even harder to understand.) Beguyer de Chancourtois had constructed what he called a "telluric screw" (Figure 6). He used a tall cylinder and subdivided its surface by sixteen vertical and parallel lines—the figure sixteen was chosen because that is the atomic weight of oxygen. He then entered the elements by their atomic weights and connected them by a line which ran like a screw thread around the cylinder; hence the name "telluric screw" meaning "the screw of the elements of *tellus*" (the earth). Then he noticed that all the elements on his screw line that fell on the same vertical line were similar chemically, as for example lithium, sodium and potassium, one of Döbereiner's triads.

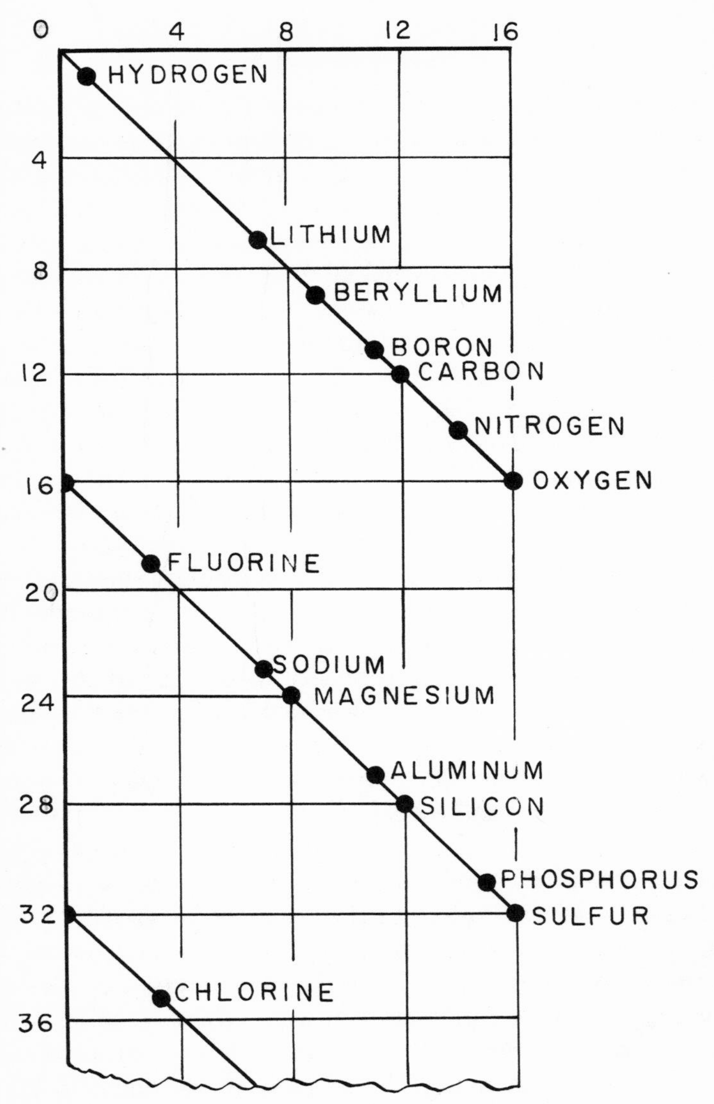

FIGURE 6. *Upper portion of the "telluric screw" of Beguyer de Chancourtois. One has to imagine that this diagram is wound around a cylinder so that the vertical line numbered 16 touches the left-hand margin. The diagonal lines then form a continuous helix or corkscrew. All then known elements fitted on that line.*

It was an interesting attempt, but a bit clumsy for easy use.

If Beguyer de Chancourtois failed to make an impression on the chemists of the day, an English chemist, John Alexander Reina Newlands (1837–1898), fared even worse. He was an analytical chemist and later became an authority on the chemistry of sugar refining. In 1864 he arranged the chemical elements then known in order of their atomic weights and saw that certain chemical properties appeared again with every eighth element. This he called the "law of octaves" and proceeded to classify the elements into families. The (British) Chemical Society would have none of it, however, and even refused to publish his paper. At one meeting another member of the society said that one could obtain such results by arranging the elements alphabetically.

The treatment given to Newlands mainly shows that the majority of the members of the society had little use for theory. They were "practical" men who did not have to think of atoms while doing their work and they did not think that theoretical knowledge of that kind could be useful to them. Later, after others had shown that it *was* useful, the tide turned, and in 1887 the Royal Society awarded Newlands the Humphry Davy Medal for his efforts.

The two who did succeed in arranging the elements in a system that was both logical and useful were a German and a Russian, both of whom had attended the Karlsruhe congress. The German was Dr. Lothar Meyer (1830–1895; in 1892 he was elevated to Lothar von Meyer), who was professor of chemistry in Karlsruhe, beginning in 1868. His doctoral dissertation had been about a subject on both chemistry and medicine ("On the Effects of Carbon Monoxide Gas on Blood") and during the Franco-Prussian war of 1870–71 he worked as a physician in an emergency hospital. Not knowing that his Russian colleague was working on the same problem, he began his arrangement of the chemical elements around the year 1865. But when the Russian chemist published his system, Dr. Meyer declared at once that he was not even finished and that he would not have gone so far.

The Russian was Dimitri Ivanovitch Mendeleyeff (1834–1907),[4] who had been born in Tobolsk, Siberia, where his father was a school principal. The son was somewhat disappointing to his father, for he showed no interest in Latin, Greek or even Old Slavonic. But he was eager to learn about mathematics and the natural sciences. Mendeleyeff's father died in 1847 and the glass factory, now the sole source of his family's income, burned down in 1848. The widow then traveled to Moscow and, with the help of connections of her late husband, succeeded in having "Dimitri Ivanitch" accepted as a student at Moscow University, with all fees paid by the Russian government and a stipend for his living expenses. Whoever had to take the responsibility for spending public funds on young Mendeleyeff never had cause to regret it, for he became the most famous Russian scientist during his lifetime and may still be the most famous one.

Arranging the elements into a system that made sense was a long and painstaking task. The atomic weights that could be found in chemical literature were not always trustworthy. Mendeleyeff had to write an endless stream of letters to individual chemists and to universities and other scientific institutions to ask for pieces of information that he might need. For eight years he collected such information, and for years he must have tried various arrangements. Finally, in 1861, he felt that his work was as complete as possible. The Russian Chemical Society published his paper, called "The Relation of the Properties to the Atomic Weights of the Elements," in the March 1861 issue of the society's journal.

[4] Pronounced De-MEE-tree Ee-VAH-no-vitch Men-day-LAY-yeff; in normal conversation the "Ivanovitch" (which indicates that his father's given name was "Ivan") is usually contracted to "Ee-VAH-nitch."

At about the same time Mendeleyeff was appointed professor of chemistry at the University of St. Petersburg (now Leningrad), and there arose a minor problem quite similar to that of Dalton's Quaker clothing. New professors at the university had to present themselves to the Czar, and a courtier was supposed to arrange the audience. That Mendeleyeff did not own a court costume did not matter in Imperial Russia. Since he did not belong to the nobility, he could not wear a court costume anyway. In his case, the problem was that his hair was long, silky and pale yellow. So was his beard. The courtier suggested with some firmness that Professor Mendeleyeff have his hair and beard suitably trimmed, saying that he would arrange an appointment with the court barber. Mendeleyeff said "no" with even greater firmness; he had his hair cut once a year and that time was several months in the future. The courtier left, flustered, and the Czar must have been amused: he received Mendeleyeff with flowing hair and beard, and they had a long discussion about the mineral resources of Russia.

Medeleyeff's table shown on page 113 does not look like the periodic table now in chemistry textbooks (see page 154). The first element, hydrogen, did not fit in well with the others, so Mendeleyeff disregarded it at first. The second element, helium, was unknown and unsuspected and Mendeleyeff started with element no. 3, lithium, which has an atomic weight of 7. The next heavier element, beryllium, had an atomic weight of 9 and the one after that, boron, had an atomic weight of 11. So far Mendeleyeff merely followed in the footsteps of Beguyer de Chancourtois, of whom he may not have known. But then he noticed that lithium had a valence of 1, beryllium of 2, boron of 3, carbon of 4. Continuing, he saw that the elements, arranged by their atomic weight, showed a set of valences running 1 – 2 – 3 – 4 – 3 – 2 – 1. After this first group of seven elements, there would follow another group whose atomic weights would grow steadily larger; but again there would be a sequence of valences running 1 – 2 – 3 – 4 – 3 – 2 – 1. Mendeleyeff called the first and the second "short period"—the reason that we still speak of the "Periodic System" of the elements. Then there came five "large periods" with 17 members each. If the columns were read from the top down, they progressed in the order of increasing atomic weight. If read from left to right (the "groups" of Mendeleyeff), there were elements with the same or a similar valence.

In arranging his table, Mendeleyeff showed considerable courage, about the same degree of courage he had displayed when he refused to have his beard trimmed "out of season." If the sequence of the atomic weights failed to obey his periods of valences, he did not hesitate to assume that the atomic weight given in the books was wrong. If the periods lacked a member, he declared that this must be an undiscovered element. He went even farther; if there was a hole in his arrangement, he predicted what the characteristics of the element would be after it had been found. He made half a dozen such predictions, and three of them were proved to be correct while he was still alive.

In one jump chemistry had outstripped the older sciences that had had useful systems of classification for many years. No zoologist had ever dared to predict the discovery of an animal because the system had room for one with some intermediate characteristics. Astronomers had made predictions of discovery from time to time and sometimes they had even been right. But chemistry, with the aid of Mendeleyeff's table, could predict and do even more; it could go looking for the missing elements because the predicted characteristics also hinted where they might be found.

Lothar Meyer, the other discoverer of the periodic system, had progressed almost as far as Mendeleyeff in working out

MENDELEYEFF'S PERIODIC TABLE
[*as published in Volume I of the first English edition of his* Principles of Chemistry]

Groups	Higher salt-forming oxides	Typical or 1st small period	Large Periods				
			1st	2nd	3rd	4th	5th
I.	R_2O	Li = 7	K 39	Rb 85	Cs 133	—	—
II.	RO	Be = 9	Ca 40	S 87	Ba 137	—	—
III.	R_2O_3	B = 11	Sc 44	Y 89	La 138	Yb 173	—
IV.	RO_2	C = 12	Ti 48	Zr 90	Ce 140	—	Th 232
V.	R_2O_5	N = 14	V 51	Nb 94	—	Ta 182	—
VI.	RO_3	O = 16	Cr 52	Mo 96	—	W 184	Ur 240
VII.	R_2O_7	F = 19	Mn 55	—	—	—	—
			Fe 56	Ru 103	—	Os 191	—
VIII.			Co 58.5	Rh 104	—	Ir 193	—
			Ni 59	Pd 106	—	Pt 196	—
I.	R_2O H = 1.	Na = 23	Cu 63	Ag 108	—	Au 198	—
II.	RO	Mg = 24	Zn 65	Cd 112	—	Hg 200	—
III.	R_2O_3	Al = 27	Ga 70	In 113	—	Tl 104	—
IV.	RO_2	Si = 28	Ge 72	Sn 118	—	Pb 206	—
V.	R_2O_5	P = 31	As 75	Sb 120	—	Bi 208	—
VI.	RO_3	S = 32	Se 79	Te 125	—	—	—
VII.	R_2O_7	Cl = 35·5	Br 80	I 127	—	—	—
		2nd small period	*1st*	*2nd*	*3rd*	*4th*	*5th*
			Large Periods				

the table. But he had not progressed to predictions and he declared that Mendeleyeff had been the first to accomplish the system. Mendeleyeff, on the other hand, never neglected to say that his work would have been done by Meyer if he, Mendeleyeff, had been prevented from finishing his own work because of sickness, accident or death. In 1882 the Royal Society awarded the Humphry Davy Medal to Mendeleyeff *and* to Meyer, and Meyer was deeply touched by the recognition. The two appeared together at various scientific gatherings.

In 1894 Meyer, who by then was Lothar von Meyer, was appointed head (*Rector magnificus* was the official title) of the University of Tübingen, at the apex of his academic career. But he had held the office for less than a year when he died suddenly of a stroke. Mendeleyeff, four years younger, had resigned his professorship one year before Meyer's death. He was satisfied with his pension because it would enable him to travel. In 1893 he went to the Exposition in Chicago,[5] and then wrote a book about future industrialization. In 1899 he went to the Ural mountains and wrote a book about the iron industry of the region with many ideas about its future development, and in 1900 he went to the Exposition in Paris. He might have hoped to meet Jules Verne, his favorite author, there. But it did not happen. Another author Mendeleyeff liked to read—or have his wife read to him—was James Fenimore Cooper, while his favorite composer was Beethoven.

In January 1907 Mendeleyeff caught a cold that developed into pneumonia. While he was sick, his wife read to him

[5] Earlier, in 1887, he had planned a balloon ascent with a Russian balloonist for the purpose of observing an eclipse of the sun. At the time of takeoff, it turned out that the balloon was too heavy; Mendeleyeff ordered the balloonist out of the gondola and, without any previous experience, flew alone and landed safely. The peasants of the area talked about this for a long time, saying: "Dimitri Ivanitch flew on a bladder and broke into heaven."

Jules Verne's story *The English to the North Pole.* As was often the case with pneumonia, it looked as if he might recover, but on February 2, 1907 he died.

It so happened that owing to a new tool of science, there was a flurry of new discoveries in the years following the Karlsruhe congress. Another such flurry occurred after Mendeleyeff's table had become known, and partly because of it.

The new tool was spectrum analysis, which had started out as a means of judging the quality of optical glass. If a beam of white light is sent through a glass prism it is drawn out into a band showing the colors of the rainbow (Figure 7). If sunlight was used and the spectrum was large enough, one could see a number of black lines. If artificial light is used, one is likely to find a number of especially bright lines in the spectrum, as Wollaston, the discoverer of palladium, noticed in 1802 when observing the spectrum of a candle flame. Wollaston described his observation carefully, but did nothing else about the phenomenon.

In 1814 a young German physicist, Joseph von Fraunhofer (1787–1826), a maker of astronomical telescopes and for this

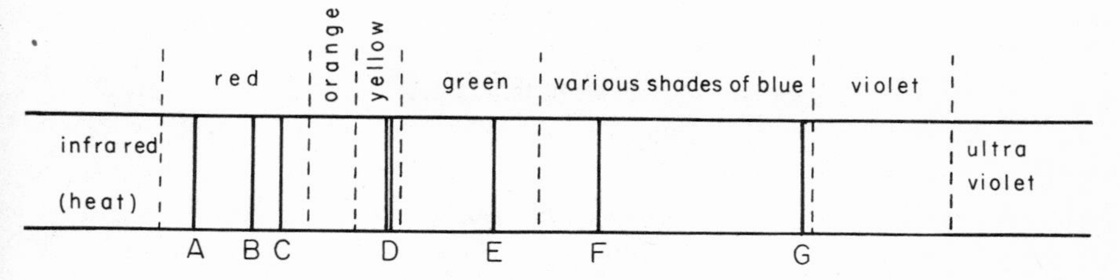

FIGURE 7. *The spectrum of our sun. The broken lines show the approximate points where the different colors begin; actually they merge into each other. The dark lines from A to G are the lines first seen by Fraunhofer in the solar spectrum and these are the original "Fraunhofer's lines." Fraunhofer did not realize their significance but used them to check the quality of optical glass.*

reason very much interested in glass and glassmaking, saw the dark lines in the solar spectrum. His first reaction was that the glass was of poor quality, but in time he convinced himself that they were real. He was not interested in their origin, since his mind was on something else, but he turned his earlier reasoning around. At first he had thought them to be due to poor quality of the glass; now he used them to judge the quality of optical glass. He picked out eight especially strong lines, located in different colors in the spectrum, and labeled them A to H for easy reference. They are now known as "Fraunhofer's lines."

One should think that it was only one step from Fraunhofer's lines to an understanding of their meaning and their utilization. It was not; it was a long and rocky road. An English scientist, Henry Fox Talbot (1800–1877), who pioneered in optics and photography and was the first to decipher Assyrian inscriptions, noticed something interesting in 1834. Both lithium and strontium salts color a flame red, but Talbot saw that the red lines produced by these two elements are in different places in the spectrum. In 1854 an American, David Alter of Freeport, Pennsylvania, experimented with prisms and wrote an article in the *American Journal of Science,* telling about the different lines he had obtained and even saying that it seemed that every element produced its specific lines.

But the "discoverers" of spectrum analysis were Strohmeyer's pupil, Robert Wilhelm Bunsen (1811–1899), and Gustav Robert Kirchhoff (1824–1887), who met Bunsen in 1851. Bunsen was, of course, a chemist, while Kirchhoff was a physicist. Gradually the two became friends and worked together. As has been mentioned repeatedly, the compounds of different elements impart a different color to a nonluminous flame, such as the flame of the Bunsen burner invented for this purpose. Bunsen was interested in describing the colors as precisely as possible and had made glass disks of various colors with which he tried to match the colors produced by the elements. While doing this, Kirchhoff had the idea that a prism might be helpful. Now the colored flames produced only a few colored lines each—and the door to new knowledge, preceded by a fantastic amount of work, had been opened.

Why were the lines sometimes luminous and sometimes black? The answer was that the light from a glowing element produced luminous lines. But if that element glows along with others, and the light then passes through the same element (say nitrogen), the light from the glowing element—and only that light—is absorbed and the lines turn black. Heating ordinary salt in the flame of a Bunsen burner produced a strong yellow double line; it was in the same place in the spectrum as Fraunhofer's black double line that he had called "D." And so it went; Kirchhoff and Bunsen examined and noted the lines from many elements, and succeeded most of the time in identifying them with black lines in the spectrum made by sunlight. They used different methods of producing very strong light; they investigated the light from so-called Geissler tubes,[6] in which small amounts of gases glowed when an electric current was sent through the apparatus.

It must have occurred to them early in their investigation that their method might lead to the discovery of new elements once the spectra of all known elements had been mapped.

The first discovery was made just about one year after Kirchhoff had suggested the use of a prism. Bunsen examined some mother liquor made from the mineral-water spring near the small town of Dürkheim and found two blue lines, close together, that did not belong to any known element. Bunsen was certain that the lines were caused by a new element, which he called "cesium"; he then tried to isolate

[6] The forerunner of the neon tubes of today, but neon had not yet been discovered.

the new element by customary chemical means and found that it was not difficult. In fact, others had had cesium sulphate before him but had thought it was potassium sulphate. However, he did not go farther than isolating cesium sulphate; the pure metal was obtained 20 years later by Dr. Carl Setterberg, who did most of the work in Bunsen's laboratory.

One of the reasons that Bunsen failed to concentrate on obtaining the metal was that only a few months later he discovered another new element which betrayed its presence by two red lines, close to the black line that Fraunhofer had called "A." Bunsen called it "rubidium," and this time he did isolate the metal. Bunsen, always aware that it was Kirchhoff's idea that had started the discoveries, never said "I discovered" but used a German phrase meaning "One has found."

The third element to be found by spectrum analysis was no longer Bunsen's. The discoverer was Sir William Crookes (1832–1919). In 1850 or 1851 Crookes (he did not become Sir William until 1897) had obtained a quantity of the mud that is the residue of the manufacture of sulphuric acid. The mud was known to contain selenium and Crookes had extracted it for his own researches. But he kept what was left over, suspecting that it might contain tellurium (which he would extract some ten years later). Crookes reasoned that there probably was still some selenium in the residue so that it could now be used to establish the lines produced by both selenium and tellurium. He established the selenium lines and, as they gradually became weaker, he waited for the tellurium lines to appear. Suddenly there was a brilliant green line, very luminous but lasting for only a second, if that long.

Whatever caused the green line seemed to evaporate quickly in the flame, so Crookes kept adding his material steadily in small doses to make the green line last longer. But that did not yet solve the problem of what it was. There were few different elements in the residue he used, and he had to find which one of them had caused the green line. If none of the known elements did, it had to be a new one. He did not have enough material for a prolonged analysis, but after he had done what he could, he felt convinced that the green line came from an unknown element, which he called "thallium." In the third issue of the *Chemical News* for 1861 (a journal he had founded himself) Crookes described in fine detail what he had done so that others would be able to see the green line, too.

There is no doubt that Crookes was the first to see the green line and must therefore be called the discoverer of thallium. But there is doubt whether he was the first to isolate the metal. A French chemist, Claude-August Lamy (1820–1878), worked on lead cistern mud from a sulphuric-acid plant at Loos in Belgium. He mixed the dry mud with the same volume of *aqua regis,* until the acid had almost evaporated, then mixed it with twice its weight of boiling water, which was permitted to cool after some time. Yellow crystals formed and these were recrystallized several times in order to purify them. Lamy then used the current from five "Bunsen cells"—the carbon-zinc battery invented by Bunsen—and obtained metallic thallium at the negative pole. He concluded his report saying, "This is the experiment by which we have, for the first time, isolated the metal."

Crookes replied that he had obtained metallic thallium in powder form as early as May 1, 1862 but had not dared to melt it into an ingot, fearing that it might boil away. A committee of chemists of the French Academy went carefully over all claims and counterclaims and agreed with Lamy that Crookes's black powder had *not* been pure thallium. Lamy got the credit for having isolated the metal first—but Crookes is still its discoverer.

The next element to be discovered by spectrum analysis

was also the discovery of two men, even though the younger of the two later tried to take all of the credit. They were Ferdinand Reich (1799–1882), professor of physics at the Freiberg School of Mines, and Hieronymus Theodor Richter (1824–1898), at the time Reich's assistant and later director of the School of Mines. Reich, incidentally, was also a Strohmeyer student and, during his study year in Paris had met Gay-Lussac (whom he especially admired), Thenard, Justus von Liebig and Alexander von Humboldt. One of Reich's activities had been to introduce the "French system of measurement"—what we now call the metric system—in Germany.

In 1863 Reich analyzed zinc ores from one of the Freiberg mines, hoping to find thallium, but he ended up with what he considered to be the sulphide of a new element. As far as Reich was concerned, the spectroscope was a useless instrument because, like Dalton, he was color blind. His assistant, Richter, had to take over. He took some of Reich's ore, placed it in the loop of a platinum wire and inserted it into the flame of a Bunsen burner. At once a brilliant blue-violet line appeared in the spectrum, not far from the blue cesium lines. Since the line is in that portion of the spectrum that is called "indigo," the name of the new element became "indium." (4)

A few more tests showed that one did not even need a spectroscope in this case; the light of an indium compound glowing in the Bunsen flame was so strong and so distinctive that it could be recognized at once.

After that Reich and Richter made pure indium and Richter, in April 1867, exhibited two specimens of about the size of a dime to the Academy of Sciences in Paris; their value was about 800 pounds sterling. Reich, being busy with other things, entrusted the thorough investigation of the new element to a younger professor at the School of Mines by the name of Clemens Winkler (1838–1904).

The reports of the discoveries of these new elements were read avidly by Mendeleyeff, who was fluent in German and

French, though poor in English. They helped him to round out his tables and they reduced the number of empty spaces.

When Mendeleyeff said that Lothar Meyer would have discovered the Periodic Table if an accident had prevented him from finishing his work, he might have added: "and if Meyer had met with an accident too, it would have been done by my French colleague, Lecoq de Boisbaudran."

Paul Émile Lecoq de Boisbaudran (1838?–1912), descended from a noble old French family, had found for himself that there was a certain regularity in the chemical behavior of the elements. He had been studying spectra since he had read the first report of Bunsen and Kirchhoff, so he had a great deal of experience when he started out on his search for a new element in 1874. His reasoning was that all the better-known minerals had been analyzed by competent chemists and, if he was to find something new, it would be in ores from out-of-the-way places.

He began with zinc ores from the Pierrefitte mines in the Pyrenees and he was, it must be said, very lucky. He dissolved the ore and put a piece of metallic zinc into the solution. A deposit formed on the zinc and he heated it in the flame of a Bunsen burner. There was no result, but Lecoq de Boisbaudran thought that a hotter flame might bring one. He used an oxyacetylene torch next, and the spectrogram showed two lines he had never seen before. A few additional tests convinced him that he did have a new element and in 1875 he announced the discovery. He named the element "gallium," in honor of his native country, since the Latin name for France had been "Gallia." [7]

So far he had not obtained the metal itself, as he did not have enough material. But two French zinc-mining societies,

[7] But there is the suspicion that he also may have been punning a bit. Gallia was the name for France, but Latin *gallus* means "rooster," and "Lecoq" means "rooster," too. "Gallium," therefore, can stand for "French metal" as well as "Lecoq's metal."

hearing about it, furnished him with several hundred kilograms of a zincblende that was suspected of containing gallium and Lecoq de Boisbaudran isolated 75 grams (about 3 ounces) of the metal. Gallium has such a low melting point (about 89° Fahrenheit) that it will become a liquid on a hot summer day, and it was much used for thermometers that had to measure temperatures higher than those for which a mercury-filled thermometer is useful.

When Lecoq de Boisbaudran discovered gallium, he was not aware of Mendeleyeff's prediction for the element eka-aluminum. But the accuracy of the prediction is staggering, as shown in the following comparison.

EKA-ALUMINUM	GALLIUM
Should be a metal with an atomic weight of about 68 and a specific gravity of 5.9, with a low melting point. It should not be affected by air and should dissolve slowly in acids and alkalies. Its oxide should have the formula Ea_2O_3; it should dissolve in acids to form salts of the type EaX_3. The hydroxide should dissolve in acids and alkalies; the sulphide should be precipitated by H_2S. The anhydrous chloride should be more volatile than zinc chloride.	A metal with the atomic weight 69.72 and a specific gravity of 5.94. The melting point is 30.15° centigrade. Unaffected by air, it dissolves slowly in acids and alkalies. The oxide is Ga_2O_3; it dissolves in acids, forming salts of the type GaX_3. The hydroxide dissolves in acids and alkalies; the sulphide is precipitated by H_2S and the anhydrous chloride is more volatile than zinc chloride.

The next discovery after gallium was also a triumph for Mendeleyeff, although the discovery was not made because someone searched for one of the elements predicted by the great Russian. In 1879 Lars Fredrik Nilson (1840–1899) worked in Berzelius's laboratory on the so-called rare-earth elements (see Chapter VIII) and came across substances that should have been compounds of the element ytterbium, but had the wrong atomic weight. Nilson concluded almost immediately that an unsuspected and possibly unknown element was present. He sent samples to Tobias Robert Thalén (1827–1905), who was not a chemist at all but an astronomer and physicist. But Thalén had a good spectroscope and knew how to use it. He reported to Nilson that he had found several lines that had never before been observed. Meanwhile, Nilson had changed his method of analysis in such a manner that he was looking for the compounds with the smallest molecular weights. His results, and Thalén's spectrogram, indicated a new element, which was named "scandium" (for Scandinavia). Per Cleve, one year later, determined its atomic weight to be 45 and immediately remembered Mendeleyeff's prediction of eka-boron. Again the agreement between prediction and discovery was fascinating:

EKA-BORON

Atomic weight should be 44; should form one oxide of the formula Eb_2O_3 with a specific gravity of 3.86. The oxide should not dissolve in alkalies and it is doubtful whether it will decompose ammonium chloride. The salts should be colorless and produce gelatinous precipitates with potassium hydroxide and sodium carbonate. The salts should not crystallize well and the carbonate should not dissolve in water. The chloride $EbCl_3$ should be less volatile than aluminum chloride.

SCANDIUM

Atomic weight is 45.10, the oxide, Sc_2O_3; it has the specific gravity 3.86, is not soluble in alkalies and does not decompose ammonium chloride. Scandium salts are colorless, their precipitates with potassium hydroxide and sodium carbonate are gelatinous. They are difficult to crystallize. The carbonate is insoluble in water. The chloride ($ScCl_3$) is far less volatile than aluminum chloride.

Clemens Winkler, the investigator of indium, was the son of a student of Berzelius and Sefström, and when he became professor at the School of Mines he was already well known for extreme neatness in his work. In the course of time he was to become the discoverer of a third element predicted by Mendeleyeff, though, in this case, Mendeleyeff was not the only one who had predicted it. Around 1862 the English chemist, Newlands, who had tried to find the "law of octaves," had said that silicon and tin had all the characteristics of a Döbereiner "triad," with the middle element missing.

In 1885 one of the Freiberg mines yielded a new mineral which obviously contained silver and was therefore called "argyrodite." Albin Weisbach, a professor at the School of Mines, who had discovered it, gave the mineral to Richter, the co-discoverer of indium, who by then was the director of the school. Richter confirmed that the mineral contained silver, sulphur and a little mercury and then Weisbach asked Winkler to make a thorough analysis. Winkler did, but found that his figures for percentages in the mixture were lower than expected. The point was, however, that they were lower than expected all the time and always by the same amount. Of course, he suspected the presence of a new element but he failed again and again to isolate it; finally, after four months of steady work, he obtained heavy white flakes which turned out to be the sulphide of the new element. It had a property that Winkler could not have foreseen—and which caused much of the delay—it dissolves easily in water and in acids diluted with water, but remains untouched by concentrated acids, the opposite of what one would suspect.

Since Lecoq de Boisbaudran had named his element "gallium," and Nilson had named his "scandium," Winkler named his own discovery "germanium." But what was germanium?

Mendeleyeff wrote a letter to the German Chemical Society, giving the properties it should have if it was the element between antimony and bismuth. However, he added, it is more likely that it is the element between cadmium and mercury. A professor, Victor von Richter, wrote to Winkler, saying that he thought it to be Mendeleyeff's eka-silicon and Lothar Meyer said the same to his students. Winkler had to make the decision but he could not make it until he had prepared more germanium compounds, which was a tedious job. But finally he could announce that it was eka-silicon.

Again, here is the comparison between prediction and discovery:

EKA-SILICON	GERMANIUM
Should be a metal with an atomic weight of about 72 and a specific gravity of 5.5. The atomic volume should be 13, its valence must be 4, and the specific heat 0.073. Its dioxide should have a specific gravity of 4.7 and a molecular volume of 22. The tetrachloride of eka-silicon should have a specific gravity of 1.9 and a boiling point below 100° centigrade. The element can be expected to have a high melting point.	A metal with the atomic weight 72.60 and a specific gravity 5.47. The atomic volume is 13.22, the valence is 4 and the specific heat 0.076. The dioxide has a specific gravity of 4.703 and a molecular volume of 22.16. The tetrachloride has a specific gravity of 1.887, its boiling point is 86° centigrade. The melting point of germanium is 958.5° centigrade.

Winkler had not only proved the existence of Mendeleyeff's eka-silicon, but he had also vindicated the poor, ridiculed Newlands; germanium was indeed the center link of a triad. It is possible that the discovery of germanium helped to convince the Royal Society that Newlands should be awarded the Davy Medal, which was done one year after the announcement of the discovery.

During the same year an outstanding French chemist,

Henri Moissan (1852–1907) succeeded in doing something that many chemists had tried to do before him, namely to isolate the element fluorine. Fluorine is a yellowish gas which will attack anything, including glass and porcelain. Its compound fluoric acid is almost as violent as the element itself; Sir Humphry Davy observed that it "immediately destroys the glass and anything of vegetable or animal origin." He suggested to other chemists that an apparatus for obtaining and collecting fluorine should be made of fluorspar, which is already a fluorine compound and therefore could not be attacked by fluorine further. Two Irish chemists, the brothers George and Thomas Knox, followed the advice, but failed to obtain fluorine and both came down with severe cases of hydrofluoric-acid poisoning. At least two chemists died while investigating fluorine, and several others had narrow escapes.

In spite of this list of casualties, of which Moissan was well aware, he began to work on fluorine in 1886 and was successful. He used platinum vessels, which resist fluorine for some time, and whatever could be made of fluorspar was made of it. After his repeated demonstrations, Moissan was rewarded with a full professorship and the La Caze Prize of 10,000 francs. But he said, on his deathbed, that fluorine had shortened his life by ten years. Since he was only fifty-five years old when he died, it might perhaps have been even twenty years.

After Moissan had finished his original research, the chemists of the Siemens Works in Berlin discovered that there was no need for the expensive platinum, for one could use copper. Of course, fluorine attacks copper immediately, but the resulting compond forms a skin that protects the metal below it.

In spite of its violence, and partly because of it, fluorine is an important element. Some of its compounds are wonderful disinfectants, if they can be applied in a manner that prevents them from destroying a lot of other things. Another fluorine compound is the gas freon, which is used for refrigeration, and there is the fluorine-carbon compound teflon that was originally created during work on the uranium bomb. And any rocket engineer knows that pure fluorine would be a powerful rocket propellant when used instead of oxygen with any of the customary fuels,—but it would take a lot of courage to use it.

VIII. RARE EARTHS AND NOBLE GASES

John William Strutt (1842–1919) became the third Baron Rayleigh at the age of thirty-one and during the same year he was made a member of the Royal Society. Five years later he became the head of the Cavendish Laboratory at Cambridge. There can be no doubt that he was an important man at a relatively early age, but he fully deserved his rapid advancement, for he was a conscientious researcher and always ready for new ideas. Professionally he was a physicist and he made many contributions to his science, most of them having to do with the atmosphere, but his best-known discovery was in the field of chemistry.

It began as a theoretical problem. Lord Rayleigh's compatriot, Prout, had had the idea that all elements might be just clusters of hydrogen atoms but several chemists had spent many years in establishing the atomic weights of the elements precisely, and they were not whole numbers; hence, they could not be tight aggregations of hydrogen atoms. Rayleigh decided to try once more; if Prout was right in spite of what others had found, and if you took hydrogen to be "1," then oxygen would have to be "16." But Rayleigh could show that oxygen was 15.882, which disproved Prout's hypothesis once more. This done, Rayleigh checked the atomic weights of the two main gases of the atmosphere, oxygen and nitrogen, and soon found that the ratio of the weights of these two gases was not always the same. Going through his laboratory notebooks, he quickly discovered the reason.

He had prepared oxygen by three different methods and his oxygen had never shown any variations. But if he had used nitrogen from the atmosphere for one experiment and then repeated the same experiment with nitrogen from ammonia, the result was different. Nitrogen from ammonia seemed to be lighter than nitrogen from the atmosphere, which, of course, was absurd. He measured the difference and found that one liter of nitrogen from the atmosphere weighed 1.257 grams, while one liter of nitrogen from ammonia weighed 1.250 grams. Since nitrogen, after all, was nitrogen, the difference had to be due to some impurity. The normal impurities in the atmosphere—water vapor, carbon dioxide and, in cities and industrial areas, sulphur dioxide—could be ruled out; they were too easy to detect and to remove. Lord Rayleigh thought of other possibilities: maybe his nitrogen from ammonia still contained a little hydrogen, which would make it lighter. But it didn't. The next thought was that the nitrogen from the atmosphere might still contain some oxygen, which would make it a little heavier. Again, it didn't.

One possibility—and Lord Rayleigh hoped that this was the case—was the existence of a new and heavier form of nitrogen that had so far escaped detection. The oxygen molecule is normally O_2, but electric sparks in the laboratory and lightning in nature can produce O_3 (ozone), which is, of course, a heavier molecule. Now nitrogen is normally N_2. Could it be that there was an N_3? Rayleigh tried to make it in the same manner in which one can make O_3, but the result was zero. If there was an N_3 it must be formed by an unknown cause. Having come to a stop in his investigations, Lord Rayleigh wrote a letter to the British scientific weekly magazine, *Nature* (it appeared in the September 29, 1892 issue), telling what had happened and asking for suggestions. Nobody said a word; nobody had ever heard of N_3.

More than a year went by. Then Professor William Ramsay (1852–1916; beginning in 1902, Sir William Ramsay) asked Lord Rayleigh's permission to carry on with the investigation of atmospheric nitrogen.

William Ramsay had been born in Glasgow, Scotland, the son of an engineer, and had shown an early interest in nature, music and books. On Sundays he had to go to church, and the sermons were both long and boring. Young William sat through them reading the Bible, but one day his parents discovered that the Bibles he was reading were French or German Bibles. Young William had discovered that one could learn another language best by reading a book that one knew very well in that language, a piece of advice that all teachers of languages give to their pupils. Later in life Ramsay spoke French, German and Italian fluently, which greatly impressed his colleagues from the European mainland.[1]

Ramsay studied in Heidelberg under Bunsen, became a

[1] I don't know whether this story is true, but I was told by one of my own professors that a German scientist, speaking English to an English scientist, remarked on Sir William Ramsay's linguistic ability, saying more or less, "You English aren't very good at languages normally." The English scientist, somewhat flustered, replied: "But my dear man, he isn't a *real* Englishman; he is Scots, you know."

professor at Bristol University in 1880 and a professor at the University of London in 1887. Why he delayed approaching Lord Rayleigh after the letter in *Nature* does not seem to be known; he may have overlooked it when it appeared, or he may have had a project of his own. At any event, when he did go to work on the problem of N_3, he and Rayleigh kept in constant touch. Ramsay remembered that Cavendish, after whom Rayleigh's laboratory was named, had also come across a discrepancy with nitrogen back in 1785. Cavendish had tried to have atmospheric nitrogen completely absorbed but there always remained a small bubble of gas, which he estimated to be $1/120$ of the original nitrogen.

Ramsay took atmospheric air, removed everything that was not nitrogen and then passed the nitrogen over red-hot magnesium to have it absorbed. Most of it was. What was left was slightly heavier than nitrogen. In volume it was $1/80$ of the original nitrogen. It was obviously the same "bubble" that had irked Cavendish and its slightly greater weight seemed to agree with Rayleigh's guess that it might be N_3. But then Ramsay used a spectroscope and saw groups of red and green lines that had not been listed by anybody (the spectrum of the gas was later studied very carefully by Sir William Crookes). At that moment Ramsay began to wonder. Maybe a tri-atomic nitrogen would produce unusual lines, but its reluctance to form chemical compounds was unusual. True, N_2 is less active chemically than O_2, but O_3 is more active than O_2. Hence, one should expect N_3 to be somewhat more active than N_2. But the so-called N_3 seemed to have a valence of zero and in May 1894 Ramsay realized that Mendeleyeff did not have a valence of zeros in his table, but that there was room for such a column in his table, a whole column of empty spaces Mendeleyeff had not suspected.

Only three weeks later, Ramsay announced the discovery of a new element, a gas that did not form compounds, and it was decided to call it "argon" (the Greek word for "lazy"). If Cavendish, over a hundred years earlier, had drawn the conclusion that his stubborn bubble was an inactive element, it would have been merely a chemical curiosity. But in Ramsay's time, because of Mendeleyeff's table, the discovery of one element of that type meant that there had to be five, or possibly six, of them. Ramsay knew what he would do next.

Lecoq de Boisbaudran in France, when he learned about the discovery of argon, also immediately said that there must be more of these gases and he predicted three more. In order to understand the value of his prediction, we have to draw up a short table of the gases as we know them now. They are:

Atomic number	*Name and chemical symbol*		*Atomic weight (measured)*	*Atomic weight (predicted by L. de B.)*
2	Helium	He	4.003	not predicted
10	Neon	Ne	20.183	20.09
18	Argon	A	39.944	36.4 ± 0.08
36	Krypton	Kr	83.7	84.01 ± 0.20
54	Xenon	Xe	131.3	132.71 ± 0.15
86	Radon	Rn	222.0	(is radioactive)

Collectively, these gases are called the "noble gases,"[2] meaning that they are "aloof" and do not combine with other elements, but we now know that the heaviest of them, krypton and xenon, can be forced into chemical compounds under high pressures and temperatures.

In looking for more elements to fill the empty column in the Periodic Table, Ramsay expected to find the next heavier

[2] Some chemists call them "inert gases," but since, in industry, carbon dioxide and especially nitrogen are often called "inert gases," the term "noble gases" is preferred.

one, the one now called "krypton." Instead, he found the lightest of them, helium, and this caused an even bigger sensation.

But where does one look for gases that must be rare and do not even form compounds? A report by the American mineralogist, William F. Hillebrand, written in 1890, furnished a possible clue. Hilleband had treated a uranium ore with acid and had seen that a gas escaped; it seemed to be nitrogen. Ramsay repeated the experiment. Since the uranium compound used by Hillebrand was not available to him at the moment, he used another one. But gas formed just the same, and Ramsay determined that it was nitrogen, mixed with argon and another gas, although the lines in the spectrum were different. But his spectroscope was not of the most advanced kind, so he sent samples of the gas to two people he knew to have good spectroscopes. They were Sir William Crookes and the astronomer, Sir Joseph Norman Lockyer (1836–1920). Both sent him joyful replies and Ramsay did not have to think of a name for the new element, because it already had one. In 1868, the French astronomer Pierre Jules César Janssen had traveled to India to observe an eclipse of the sun and had found a yellow line in the solar spectrum which he called D_3. It was close to Fraunhofer's line D but not identical with it. Sir Norman Lockyer checked Janssen's report and found that the D_3 line did not match anything known. He concluded that there was an element in the sun that did not occur on earth. Because the Greek sun god was named "Helios," he called it "helium." It was this helium that Ramsay had discovered on earth!

Helium had been entirely unexpected on earth and there had been many who also doubted its existence in the sun. When the newly discovered gas was entered in the Periodic Table, it became clear that the "zero column," as it was then called, had to have a gas between helium and argon, the one now called "neon," predicted by Lecoq de Boisbaudran to have an atomic weight of about 20.

After the discovery of helium, Ramsay acquired an assistant, Dr. Morris William Travers, a native of London. They were determined to find the gas that fell between helium and argon, and also the gas beyond argon. Since helium had been found in a mineral then thought to be rare, they began heating other rare minerals. They had no success, however. Perhaps these other gases were mixed with the argon of the atmosphere, they thought. So they began to separate quantities of argon, and since it forms almost one percent of the atmosphere, it is not really a rare gas. On May 30, 1898, examining with a spectroscope what was left of air after all oxygen and nitrogen had been removed, they found the gas krypton, which betrayed itself by a greenish-yellow line and a bright green line. This was the gas beyond argon on the Periodic Table. Now they kept looking for the gas that was lighter than argon but heavier than helium. They liquefied the argon they had with liquid air, then permitted it to return to the gaseous state and caught that fraction which became a gas first. And in June of 1898 they beheld for the first time the red glow we know so well from neon signs. Neon had been discovered.

Now they knew how to proceed to find the last of the gases. They prepared as much krypton as they could, liquefied it, let it evaporate and this time caught and investigated what had evaporated last. It was xenon, discovered on July 12, 1898.

The gas at the bottom of the "zero column" was not discovered along with the others and, because it is one of the radioactive elements, it should properly be discussed in the next chapter. But its story is short, so it might as well be told here. During the very early researches on radium, it had seemed that the air that had touched radium had become radioactive itself. Nobody could say that this was strange, because everything connected with radium was new and strange. The German professor, Friedrich Ernst Dorn (1848–1916), after a number of experiments of his own, found the true explanation: radium gave off radiation and a gas that is also radioactive. The gas does not combine with anything and has its proper place below xenon. But since it is radioactive, it does not last but changes into other substances. At first it was named "niton" ("shining") but later the name was changed to "radon" to show its relationship to radium. Ramsay, assisted by Robert W. Gray, determined its atomic weight in 1910, showing that it is the heaviest gas known.[3]

Just as the noble gases have a common bond in their extreme reluctance to form chemical compounds, so another group of elements, the rare earths, have a common bond, in that they are reluctant to be separated from each other. Chemists have dubbed them the "Fraternal Fifteen" for this reason; but it should be said at once that the rare earths are not really rare and that the number fifteen can be disputed.

The problem with their number is that, technically, the rare earths form the series of elements called "the lanthanides," after the name of their first member. As the list in the appendix shows, there are fifteen elements in this series. But one of them—promethium—is radioactive and so unstable that it does not exist in nature, so there are really only fourteen. On the other hand, the element yttrium, though not one of the lanthanides, has most of the characteristics of a rare-earth metal, and even occurs in conjunction with them much

[3] In 1904 Sir William Ramsay received the Nobel Prize for his discovery of the noble gases.

of the time, so it could be called upon to substitute for the unstable promethium to bring the number up to fifteen again.

Yttrium, the almost-member of the group, had been discovered in 1794, and cerium, the most abundant of these elements, in 1803. The next one to be discovered was lanthanum, by Carl Gustaf Mosander (1797–1858), in 1839. Mosander was one of Berzelius' assistants who, like so many other early chemists, had come to chemistry via pharmacy and medicine. The discovery of cerium by Berzelius and Hisinger had indicated that there was still a great deal to be discovered about and in these minerals. Mosander wanted to try and his first experiments proved to him that the minerals ceria and yttria were very complex substances. In ceria he found another "earth," which, at the suggestion of Berzelius, was called "lanthana." The investigation was tedious and took time, and Mosander was irked by all the difficulties he encountered. Minerals that were evidently different were dissolved by the same acids and Mosander hunted around for an acid—or anything else—that would dissolve one and not the other.

In the meantime Wöhler was waiting for results because he wanted to publish them in his chemical journal; Berzelius was caught in the middle and did his best to keep the impatient Wöhler and the much irked Mosander quiet. Finally, in 1841, Mosander announced that he had obtained still another earth from lanthana, which he called "didymia" (which means "twin") because it always accompanied lanthana and could hardly be separated from it. In fact, he never succeeded completely and we now know the reason. Mosander thought that his rose-colored didymia was the oxide of a metal which, when separated, would receive the name "didymium." In reality it was a mixture of the oxides of four metals: praseodymium, neodymium, samarium and gadolinium, all of them unknown at the time.

Things went very slowly. In 1843 Mosander found that

yttria, from which all ceria, lanthana and didymia had been removed, still consisted of three different oxides. One was whitish and Mosander retained the name "yttria" for it. One was yellow and Mosander called it "erbia," while the third one was rose-colored and was named "terbia"—all names derived from the place name of Ytterby.

As if the situation were not difficult enough, French researchers, also striving for a separation of these substances, began calling the rose-colored oxide "erbia" and the yellow one "terbia" so that somebody who wanted to find out what had been done in this field had to keep in mind steadily who had written a certain report and when it had been written.

A number of years later, in 1878, the Swiss chemist, Jean Charles Galissard de Marignac (1817–1894), took erbia (the rose-colored) and separated still another oxide out of it, which he named "ytterbia." One year after that, the Swedish chemist, Per Teodor Cleve (1840–1905), investigated what was left after ytterbia and scandia had been removed. He found two more distinct substances, naming them "thulia" and "holmia." The next step was taken by an Austrian; Baron Carl Auer von Welsbach (1858–1929) split didymia into praseodymia and neodymia.[4] Then Lecoq de Boisbaudran obtained the rare earths samaria and dysprosia. If these chemists still had to work only with the means and methods available to Berzelius, they would not have been able to proceed so far. But the spectroscope at least told them what substances they had under observation, even if they had all the difficulties with separation.

One chemist, tired of hearing of more and more elements from the original ceria and yttria, paraphrased the Bible by

[4] Auer von Welsbach was a pupil of Bunsen and, when he held a piece of lanthanum oxide into the flame of a Bunsen burner one day and saw a surprisingly strong white light emitted by it, the seed for his later invention of the gas mantle was planted. His gas mantles illuminated the homes of large cities for decades, and the housewives who ignited their gas burners with a friction lighter used another one of his inventions.

saying: "And ceria begat lanthana and didymia, didymia begat praseodymia and neodymia, samaria and gadolinia; while erbia begat holmia, thulia, ytterbia and scandia. And so on, and so forth." (Figure 8)

Needless to say that countless mistakes were made, that different researchers discovered the same oxides and could not agree who had done it first, that the correction of one mistake often led to another one. For this reason it is useless to tell the detailed story of each of these elements; let us just look at what is now known, with the discovery dates and the names of discoverers that are accepted, after long search, by the Atomic Energy Commission:

Atomic number: [5]	*Name and chemical symbol:*		*Year of discovery:*	*Discoverer:*
57	Lanthanum	La	1839	Mosander
58	Cerium	Ce	1803	Klaproth, Berzelius, Hisinger (independently)
59	Praseodymium	Pr	1885	Auer von Welsbach
60	Neodymium	Nd	1885	Auer von Welsbach
61	Promethium	Pm	1947	Marinsky, Glendenin and Coryell (jointly)
62	Samarium	Sm	1879	Lecoq de Boisbaudran
63	Europium	Eu	1889	Sir William Crookes
64	Gadolinium	Gd	1880	J. C. G. de Marignac
65	Terbium	Tb	1843	Mosander ("erbium")
66	Dysprosium	Dy	1886	Lecoq de Boisbaudran
67	Holmium	Ho	1879	P. T. Cleve and J. L. Soret (jointly)
68	Erbium	Er	1843	Mosander ("terbium")
69	Thulium	Tm	1879	P. T. Cleve
70	Ytterbium	Yb	1878	J. C. G. de Marignac
71	Lutetium	Lu	1907	Georges Urbain and Auer von Welsbach (independently)

[5] The meaning and the importance of the atomic number will be explained in the next chapter.

37 Rb	38 Sr	39 Y	40 Zr	41 Nb	42 Mo	~~43~~	44 Ru	45 Rh	46 Pd
55 Cs	56 Ba	RARE EARTH METAL	~~72~~	73 Ta	74 W	~~75~~	76 Os	77 Ir	78 Pt
~~87~~	88 Ra	89 Ac	90 Th	~~91~~	92 U	~~93~~	~~94~~	~~95~~	~~96~~

RARE EARTH ELEMENTS

La	Ce	Pr	Nd	~~X~~	Sm	~~X~~	Gd	Tb	Dy	Ho	Er	Tm	Yb	~~X~~
57	58	59	60	61	62	63	64	65	66	67	68	69	70	71

FIGURE 8. *The bottom three rows of the atomic table as they would have been drawn in 1906. Crossed out spaces are those of elements not then discovered.*

The best-known example of the practical use of rare-earth elements, Auer von Welsbach's gas mantle, is now a thing of the past, although his cerium-iron "flint" is still in use. But there are many uses of these elements in which they do their jobs invisibly. Lanthanum oxide improves optical glass far beyond anything Fraunhofer might have thought possible. A mixture of rare-earth elements improves the steadiness of arc lamps in searchlights. Goggles of glass containing neodymium are used by glass blowers; such goggles swallow up all the radiation that could harm the eyes, but still give the workman a clear picture of what he is doing.

As for gadolinium (which has the strange characteristic of being attracted by a magnet at temperatures below 58° Fahrenheit but not at higher temperatures) and a few others, they have proved their value in atomic-energy research.

It is now possible to produce each of the oxides of the rare-earth metals in quantity by so-called ion exchange methods.

Obtaining the metals, if wanted, from their oxides also no longer presents any difficulties.

A final word about the "rarity" of the misnamed rare earths: the most abundant of them, cerium, is more abundant than lead; and even the least abundant, thulium, is still more abundant than gold. If new industrial uses for these metals should be discovered, there will be no shortage of the raw material.

IX. RADIOACTIVITY AND NEW CONFUSION

The story of radioactivity really began in the Physics Laboratory of the University of Würzburg in Bavaria in 1895. The professor of physics was a Dr. Wilhelm Conrad Röntgen (1845–1923), who, at that time, had already passed his fiftieth birthday. He was a tall, aristocratic-looking man with a magnificent beard but even his very best friends would not have claimed on the occasion of his fiftieth birthday that he was a famous man. Other physicists knew of him, of course, and knew that he was a competent and careful researcher, but his name held no meaning for anyone in other fields of science or to the public at large.

One single discovery, however, begun on November 5, 1895, changed all of this. On that day Professor Röntgen, experimenting with a so-called Hittorf tube (not a Crookes tube, as is stated so often) received the first indication that a type of radiation existed that had not been noticed before. In mathematics, the letter X is used to designate something unknown, so Röntgen referred to these new rays as "X rays," and they are still called that in the English-speaking countries. (But in all other countries they are called "Röntgen rays.") When the word "X rays" is mentioned, one usually thinks of broken bones, of bullets lodged somewhere in the body of the victim, of kidneystones and other medical matters. Actually, X rays have played an even more important role in scientific research. They led directly to the discovery of radioactivity.

Like every other physicist in the world, the French physicist, Antoine Henri Becquerel (1852–1908), was enormously intrigued by the discovery of the X rays, for to physicists, this was as amazing as finding helium, the sun element on earth, had been to chemists.

Becquerel, like his father, who had also been a physicist, was especially interested in fluorescent substances. Some minerals absorb light of one color and reradiate it in another color. This is especially impressive if the original radiation that is absorbed is ultraviolet, which the eye cannot see. It so happened that the first paragraph of Röntgen's account on X rays mentioned such a substance. It read:

> If we pass the discharge from a large Ruhmkorff coil through a Hittorf [tube] . . . and cover the tube with a closely fitting mantle of thin black cardboard, we observe in a completely darkened room that a paper screen washed with barium-platino-cyanide lights up brilliantly and fluoresces equally well whether the treated side or the other be turned toward the discharge tube. Fluorescence is still observable 2 meters away from the apparatus.

Many other physicists simply imitated Röntgen's experiments. Since every physics laboratory had a Ruhmkorff coil and an evacuated tube of some kind, nothing new needed to be bought or made. Becquerel, however, tried another approach, on the assumption that fluorescence and X rays might be related. In February 1896 he wrapped a photographic plate in black paper that was impenetrable both to visible and to ultraviolet light. Then he placed a fluorescing mineral on top of the wrapped plate and put them both in the sunlight so that the sun could induce the fluorescence. After some time he developed the plate and, as he expected, found it to be fogged. Aha! Fluorescence was indeed accompanied by X rays. He prepared another experiment, but the month was February and the place was Paris: there were cloudy skies, rain, and sometimes snow flurries; in any event, no sunlight. The wrapped plate and the mineral were waiting in Becquerel's drawer, and on March 1, feeling frustrated, Becquerel developed the plate, hoping that a little of the fluorescence had been left. To his surprise, he found that the plate was heavily fogged.

Becquerel immediately realized that his original assumption had been wrong. Some kind of radiation was coming from that mineral (it was a uranium compound) even when it did not fluoresce.

Studying these rays, Becquerel found that they resembled X rays in their ability to penetrate substances. Then, in 1899, he discovered that his radiation could be deflected by a magnet. Since a magnet can only influence particles, this meant that it had to consist of charged particles, or at least some of it had to be particles. What surprised him most was that the mineral kept on sending out its radiation; the intensity seemed to remain the same week after week, month after month, year after year. A brilliant young woman in Paris, Madame Marie Curie, dubbed the phenomenon "radioactivity" in 1898, the term now generally accepted, but for a number of years the radiation from uranium was called

"Becquerel's rays." In 1901 Becquerel identified the uranium in his compound as being the active element responsible for the steady stream of rays.

During the five years that had gone by since Becquerel found his "unexposed" plate fogged, there had been furious activity in the field of radioactive substances, with the French taking the lead at first. The French physicist, Pierre Curie (1859–1906), discoverer of the phenomenon called "piezo-electricity" [1] had met a Polish girl, the daughter of a physics teacher and a principal of a girls' school, by the name of Marie Sklodowska (1867–1934). In 1895 Pierre Curie obtained his doctorate and married the Polish girl, who was now Madame Marie Sklodowska-Curie. Intrigued by Becquerel's work, the Curies decided to study the minerals that fogged photographic plates. They soon realized that the radiation from these minerals was about proportional to the number of uranium atoms in the compound. The important word in that sentence is "about," for some minerals released more radiation than could be accounted for by their uranium content. Uranium had been originally discovered by the good Professor Klaproth, in pitchblende from Joachimsthal. If that pitchblende contained additional elements—the Curies must have thought of what had happened with the mineral from Ytterby—they would need a lot of pitchblende to find out.

The inspector general of the Joachimsthal mines was perfectly willing to part with leftover pitchblende; after the silver had been extracted, it did not interest him anymore. He would not charge at all for the material, he said generously, but the Curies had to pay the freight charges, which represented a large sum as far as they were concerned. But once they had the raw material, they were spectacularly

[1] Some crystals, when squeezed or stretched, generate electric current. ("Piezo" is from the Greek for "squeeze.")

successful, even though they worked under miserable conditions in a wooden shack with a leaky roof. On July 18, 1898, they announced to the French Academy of Science that they had discovered a new element, which they had named, in honor of Madame Curie's native country, "polonium." On December 26 of the same year they were able to announce the discovery of an even more strongly radiating element, which they named "radium" (from Latin *radius,* meaning "ray"). It was found out later that radium was not only very active in the sense of radioactivity, but also exceptionally active in the chemical sense. Soon after the discovery of polonium and radium, Madame Curie found that thorium, long-known, was radioactive, too.

And in 1899 another Frenchman, André Debierne (1874–1953), while busy with rare-earth elements, discovered still another radioactive element; he named it "actinium." Three years later, in 1902, the German industrial chemist, Friedrich Giesel, discovered an element that he called "emanium." However, it turned out to be the same substance as actinium. According to Otto Hahn, Giesel's description of the chemical characteristics was better than Debierne's, but Debierne had done it earlier so the name he chose is the accepted one.

Madame Curie's polonium was rediscovered by another researcher and named "radium-F," while the German chemist, Willy Marckwald, discovered it once more and called it "radio-tellurium." Professor Marckwald had history on his side because Mendeleyeff had predicted the existence of a *Dvi-Tellur* ("second tellurium") with a probable atomic weight of 212 and a probable density of 9.3. Later, Marckwald gave in, accepting the fact that radio-tellurium was the same element as polonium.

Chemists were in agreement as to where these new elements belonged in the Periodic Table, although they did not agree about the order in which they should be added. Finding out what their order should be was a minor problem which would be solved by more hard work. But this problem faded in the presence of a much bigger one. The uranium in Becquerel's minerals shot out tiny charged particles that were then identified with the electrons that raced through evacuated Crookes tubes and caused X rays if they struck a heavy piece of metal. Radium gave off the gas niton (or radon), which then changed into something else; it was not yet known what it was. And there could be no doubt that several of these radioactive elements gave off helium, another element. These new heavyweight elements obviously were unstable, which meant that their atoms were unstable. But this meant that atoms were not indivisible, as their name said. They had to have a structure of some kind consisting of subatomic particles.

The logic of the situation was clear, but we should go back to our earlier definitions for a moment. A molecule of a compound has to consist of at least two different atoms. If you separate these two atoms, you obtain atoms of elements, and the compound disappears. But if an atom consists of smaller particles, and if it is possible to separate the particles that form an atom, then the atom, and with it the element, will disappear; the subatomic particles that form atoms should be all alike no matter from what element they come.

By the year 1905 there could be no doubt anymore that the atoms of the radioactive elements were not stable and Sir Ernest Rutherford (1871–1937)—or, from 1931 until his death, Baron Rutherford of Nelson—was the first to classify the types of radiation emitted. He called them "alpha," "beta" and "gamma" rays and at one point he used a comparison that is easy to remember. When a heavy atom releases radiation, he said, it is similar to the firing of a howitzer. The shell fired is the heavy and material alpha particle. The smoke that follows the shell, still material but much lighter, is the beta particles, while the flash, bright and immaterial, is the gamma radiation.

We now know, as Rutherford suspected quite early, that the alpha particle is the same as the nucleus of a helium atom,[2] the beta particles are electrons, and the gamma rays, finally, are especially penetrating X rays.

Ernest Rutherford was born in New Zealand at a place called Nelson. He studied in England and then went to McGill University in Montreal, Canada, where he began the researches that later made him famous. In 1901 he was joined by Frederick Soddy (1877–1956), who had studied at Oxford University. Soddy made the chemical analyses as he and Rutherford studied the "emanation" from thorium. First, they found that the emanation did not come from the thorium directly, but from a different substance, which they called "thorium-X." Soddy found that the emanation was a gas like argon (actually it was radon) and he said to Rutherford: "Rutherford, this is transmutation: the thorium is disintegrating and turning itself into an argon gas." Rutherford replied: "For Mike's sake, Soddy, don't call it 'transmutation.' They'll have our heads off as alchemists." Although they were convinced that one element actually changed into another, they phrased it carefully in their joint report for the *Transactions of the Chemical Society*. After reporting the facts, they said, "Radioactivity is a manifestation of subatomic chemical change."

Sir William Crookes said that this idea "undermined the atomic theory of chemistry, revolutionized the foundations of physics and revived the ideas of the alchemists," but facts were facts and he published the report in his own *Chemical*

[2] Which is why helium forms in the course of radioactive decay. The helium nucleus picks up the two electrons it needs to become a complete helium atom.

News. But there was no violent controversy over the discovery as one might now assume. The news was received quietly, if sometimes with much skepticism, and most chemists seem to have felt that all this, since it only concerned a few recently discovered elements at the upper end of the scale, was far less important than their own researches on *stable* atoms, which did not change.

Soddy, after his work with Rutherford, returned to England and joined Sir William Ramsay, who summed up his feelings in a short poem:

> So the atoms in turn, we now clearly discern,
> Fly to bits with the utmost facility;
> They wend on their way, and, in splitting, display
> An absolute lack of stability.

He wrote this in 1905, but delayed publication until 1930, when the idea of atomic instability was accepted by everybody.

When Soddy left McGill University to return to England and Ramsay, Rutherford acquired a new assistant, who had worked in Ramsay's laboratory. His name was Otto Hahn. Hahn had been born in Frankfurt am Main, had studied organic chemistry and received his doctorate from the University of Marburg, and had become interested in radioactivity. Ramsay was in the habit of leaving his coworkers alone. He would give them an assignment and then wait for them to report; of course, he was always available for consultation. While left alone in this manner, Hahn discovered a new element, which he called "radio-thorium," and Ramsay saw to it that the discovery was published. In 1905 Hahn went to Canada and soon came across another new element, mesothorium. At a later date he found that he had a mixture of two elements, which were called "mesothorium-1" and "mesothorium-2." At the same time, the American chemist and physicist, Bertram Borden Boltwood (1870–1927), had become convinced of the validity of Rutherford's theory, that one radioactive element produced another one and that that one went on to make still another. Boltwood stated that the process seemed to start with uranium. Uranium then turned into ionium (discovered by Boltwood) and the ionium turned into radium. Radium then went through several stages and finally ended up as lead, which was stable.

Otto Hahn, having returned to Germany in 1907, was especially interested in thorium and came to the conclusion that thorium formed a similar chain, also ending up in lead. To indicate where the lead had originated, a distinction was made between "radium-lead" and "thorium-lead."

The researchers who discovered more and more rare-earth elements and those who discovered more and more radioactive elements did not work together, but their activities had the same result: they ruined Mendeleyeff's Periodic Table. Nobody knew how to fit the rare earths into the table, and the researchers on radioactivity piled up such a number of new elements that there was simply no room for them. Nobody could doubt the results that had been obtained, but Mendeleyeff's table could not accommodate these results.

Those chemists who did not work in the field of radioactivity were hardly interested. The reason was that they, the true chemists, worked with substances one could see, five grams of this, 23 grams of that, heat with 400 grams of hydrochloric acid, and so on. The "radiochemists," as they were called, always insisted that their "samples" were too small to be seen, even too small to be weighed. All they did was measure radiation and they drew conclusions from these measurements. Chemists could not quite grasp that idea, and even the great Emil Fischer, the head of the Chemical Laboratory of the University of Berlin, once said to Otto Hahn that one might have samples too small to be seen, but it was his experience that invisible amounts of chemicals usually could still be detected by their smell.

Those chemists who did work with radioactive substances felt more or less helpless. Here was a mixture of two substances that could be told apart by their radiations; one emitted gamma rays only, while the other produced beta rays (that is, electrons). But it was impossible to separate these two clearly different substances by chemical means. And the amounts were too small even to be investigated with a spectroscope. Meanwhile, they found more and more elements that did not fit Mendeleyeff's table. It was Frederick Soddy who, in 1913, suddenly realized the nature of the trouble. The 40-odd radioactive elements that had been found differed from each other in type and in intensity of radiation. But many of them had the same *chemical* characteristics and Mendeleyeff's table was based on *chemical* characteristics only. Hence, all the new "elements" were not true chemical elements. Considered from the point of view of their chemistry, there were only a few of them. Thus, the radioactive "elements" were to be assigned places in the table in accordance to their chemistry, not their radiation. They then fitted, because many of them belonged in the same place. Greek for "same place" is *isos topos;* the concept of "isotopes" had been born.

This idea not only saved the day; it also saved the useful Periodic Table. During the years that Soddy was feeling his way toward the concept of isotopes (Otto Hahn, later in his life, felt that he had come close to the concept of isotopes several times during his life but that he had always been too busy experimenting to follow through), another Rutherford pupil made a fundamental improvement of the Periodic Table itself. He was Henry Gwyn-Jeffreys Moseley (1887–

1915), the son of a distinguished English zoologist. Unfortunately, Moseley died at an early age; he was only twenty-seven, during the First World War, when he was shot by a Turkish sharpshooter.

But before Moseley's contribution can be explained, the structure of the atom should be discussed. When Rutherford and Soddy realized that something was going on *inside* the atom, they were forced to speculate about the probable appearance of an atom. Nobody had thought much about the question of what an atom might look like, although chemists would have said that they must be perfect spheres, somewhat like sub-sub-submicroscopic ball bearings. Rutherford conceived what later came to be called the "nuclear atom," an atom consisting of a small but massive nucleus and an electron at some distance. Gradually the idea was refined. The nucleus carried a positive electric charge, the electron a negative one. The simplest atom, the hydrogen atom, had a single nuclear particle, called "proton," in its center and a single electron going around it. Other, heavier atoms had a nucleus consisting of, say, seven protons, with seven electrons around the nucleus, like planets orbiting the sun. This was not quite correct, but nobody had yet advanced a better idea.

Now we can go back to Henry Gwyn-Jeffreys Moseley. He studied at Eton and Trinity College, Oxford, receiving his master's degree in 1910. Then he went to Manchester, where Rutherford was teaching, and served the University of Manchester for two years as a lecturer in physics. After that, with the aid of a fellowship, he did his own research. At the time it was vaguely known that all X rays were not the same; the difference seemed to be caused by the "target." As has been explained, X rays are produced when a beam of electrons strikes a piece of solid matter, this solid matter being called the "target." For reasons of convenience targets were made of metal because metals are good conductors of electric currents. And for reasons of durability metals with high melting points were preferred as the material for targets. It was thought that it should be possible to obtain the equivalent of a spectrum with X rays and it was likely that targets of different metals would produce different X-ray spectra.

Moseley, with the assistance of C. G. Darwin (a grandson of Charles Darwin), first mapped the X-ray spectrum of platinum, because an available X-ray tube had a platinum target. Then he tested another metal and, seeing that he did get X-ray spectra that could be clearly distinguished, he systematically took the X-ray spectra of more than 60 different elements. Moseley had numbered the known elements and had followed Mendeleyeff's system of going by atomic weights; now he found that there was a direct relationship between the frequency of the X rays emitted and the atomic number. It was suspected right then that the atomic number indicated the number of electrons around a given nucleus; now we know that the atomic number reflects the number of positive charges in the nucleus.[3] Moseley's discovery hardly changed Mendeleyeff's table, but now there could be no more quibbling where cobalt had to be placed in the table. It was now element no. 27 and it belonged between element no. 26 (iron) and element no. 28 (nickel). There had been quibbling in this case because the atomic weight of cobalt is slightly higher than the atomic weight of nickel. Now a perfect table could be drawn up (Figure 9).

More important still, since every element could be identified with a number, one could say which numbers were still missing. Moseley had identified all known elements between

[3] At very high temperatures an atom may lose one or several electrons but its atomic number is not changed.

no. 13 (aluminum) and no. 79 (gold) and there were three missing: nos. 43, 61 and 75. It was useless to search elsewhere. There could be no element, for instance, between no. 33 (arsenic) and no. 34 (selenium), since an atom could not very well have half a charge.

Still more important, it could be predicted how the X-ray spectra of these missing elements would look.

Other researchers, especially Georges Urbain in France, were enormously impressed, and in 1914 Urbain journeyed to England to learn the techniques from Moseley. Before that, Urbain, who had already discovered lutetium, believed that he had found the element that would fit into the table below zirconium, the one Moseley was to call element no. 72. He had named it "celtium," but there were doubts at once, for Urbain had discovered his celtium in rare-earth minerals and element no. 72 would not be one of the rare-earth metals. Moseley's analysis proved to Urbain that he had been mistaken, but that only increased his enthusiasm for the new method.

The real element no. 72 was not discovered until 1923—twelve years after Urbain's mistaken announcement—by Professors Georg von Hevesy, a Hungarian, and Dirk Coster, of the Royal University of Groningen, The Netherlands. Both of them were working in Copenhagen at the time and they found the new element in zirconium ores by X-ray analysis. They named it "hafnium." It is not at all rare; in fact, it is more abundant than silver. But it is so similar to zirconium that chemists simply had not noticed the difference.

During the years between the mistaken and the actual discovery of element no. 72, another hole in the table had been filled, in an area Moseley had not investigated. It was element no. 91, between no. 90 (thorium) and no. 92 (uranium), where Mendeleyeff had said that an element with an atomic weight of about 235 should exist.

IA	IIA	IIIB	IVB	VB	VIB	VIIB	VIII B		
1 H									
3 Li	4 Be								
11 Na	12 Mg								
19 K	20 Ca	21 Sc	22 Ti	23 V	24 Cr	25 Mn	26 Fe	27 Co	28 Ni
37 Rb	38 Sr	39 Y	40 Zr	41 Cb	42 Mo	43 Tc	44 Ru	45 Rh	46 Pd
55 Cs	56 Ba	57 to 71	72 Hf	73 Ta	74 W	75 Re	76 Os	77 Ir	78 Pt
87 Fr	88 Ra	89 to 103	104	105	106	107			
			UNDISCOVERED...						

FIGURE 9. *Mendeleyeff's Periodic Table as it now looks. For the arrangement of elements nos. 57–71 and 89–103, see Fig. 12. The elements to the right of the "staircase" are the nonmetals.*

Among the many elements, actually just isotopes, that the early researchers in the field of radioactivity had discovered there was one which Sir William Crookes had called "uranium-X." In 1913 Kasimir Fajans, originally of Warsaw, and O. H. Göhring, of Karlsruhe, showed that uranium-X, by

NONMETALS

IB	IIB	IIIA	IVA	VA	VIA	VIIA	VIIIA NOBLE GASES
							2 He
		5 B	6 C	7 N	8 O	9 F	10 Ne
		13 Al	14 Si	15 P	16 S	17 Cl	18 A
29 Cu	30 Zn	31 Ga	32 Ge	33 As	34 Se	35 Br	36 Kr
47 Ag	48 Cd	49 In	50 Sn	51 Sb	52 Te	53 I	54 Xe
79 Au	80 Hg	81 Tl	82 Pb	83 Bi	84 Po	85 At	86 Rn

emitting beta rays, changes into another element, which they named "brevium." The name was derived from the Latin *breve* (short) because it did not exist for long. It had a "half-life" of only 1.14 minutes.

In the vocabulary of the atomic physicist, "half-life" is one of the most important terms. Soon after radioactivity had been discovered, researchers wondered whether the intensity or the rate of radiation from such a substance could be influenced in any way. Radioactive compounds were heated to red heat, and then to white heat, but the radiation remained the same. Then the compounds were dipped in chilled alcohol that was much colder than ice water, and after that they were immersed in liquid air, which was much colder still. But no rate of change could be found. Radiochemists—as these researchers called themselves—measured the rate of radiation of a nearly pure radioactive element. Then they made compounds of this element with other elements that were not radioactive; the more complicated the compounds, the better they liked them. The rate of radiation was measured again, but that rate was still the same, considering the percentage of the radioactive element in the compound. So it did not matter whether a radioactive element was at *minus* 300° Fahrenheit or at *plus* 2,200° Fahrenheit, whether it was part of a liquid compound or a solid compound; nothing could influence the rate of radioactivity of a radioactive element. The breakdown of the atoms, or rather their nuclei, was unchanging.

But that did not mean that the various *different* radioactive elements broke down at the same rate. They didn't and so one had to find a way of describing that rate. Rutherford introduced the idea of the "half-life." The half-life, expressed in minutes, hours, days or years (whichever was most convenient in a given case) meant the time after which half of the atoms of the substance had broken down and changed into another element.

Why half-life? Why not say how long a radioactive element would last? The answer to that question is that it is impossible to say how long such an element will last and the reason for that impossibility can best be shown by a simple calculation.

Let us say that we have 1,000 atoms of the radioactive element X. The half-life of element X is known to be precisely one day, or 24 hours. Now this means that after 24 hours only 500 atoms of element X are still element X, the other 500 have become something else. After another day only 250 atoms of element X are left, after another day only 125 atoms and after the next day only 63 atoms. After the fifth day the number is down to 32, after the sixth day to 16, after the seventh day there are only 8, after the eighth day just 4, after the ninth day we have only 2, on the tenth day one of these 2 breaks down and on the eleventh day the last one of them.

Haven't we just proved that the lifetime of element X is 11 days?

No, we haven't, because all we have to do now is to assume that we start out with 10,000 atoms instead of 1,000. This time 5,000 atoms are left after the first day, but after the ninth day we have 20 atoms instead of 2, so obviously the element sample that began with 10,000 atoms will last longer than the smaller sample. That's the reason why one cannot speak about the "lifetime" of a radioactive element, because that lifetime would depend on the amount, while the half-life is the same and does not depend on how much you happen to have.

Now we can continue the strange story of element no. 91. Otto Hahn, after having worked with Ramsay in England and with Rutherford in Canada, had returned to Germany in 1907 and faced a number of difficulties. He could start out on one of two different careers, either going into industry as a chemist or beginning an academic career. Originally he had intended to become an industrial chemist, but after working in Ramsay's and Rutherford's laboratories, a job in industry looked very dull to him. But there was no academic career for him either. The normal procedure would have been to become a so-called *Privatdozent* at a university; the term can be translated as "private lecturer." A *Privatdozent* (who was not paid by the university) hoped to establish a reputation so that a university would give him a professorship.

When Otto Hahn talked to Emil Fischer, the head of the Chemical Laboratory of the University of Berlin and professor of chemistry at the same university, he ran into a difficulty he apparently had not expected. His specialty, because of the time he had spent with Ramsay and Rutherford, was "radiochemistry," but no university taught this new science. And because there was no professorship in radiochemistry anywhere, one could not become a *Privatdozent* in this specialty. But Fischer was as generous as he could be, and he permitted Hahn to follow his specialty in the university's chemistry laboratory; Fischer was willing to think that this new specialty might become a science of its own one day.

At that time, Otto Hahn met a young physicist, Dr. Lise Meitner. She was the daughter of a Viennese lawyer and had come to Berlin to take a few advanced courses. Since these courses did not take much of her time and the new field of radiochemistry interested her (because it was a borderland between physics and chemistry), she offered to help Hahn. Hahn passed this information on to Emil Fischer and Fischer was horrified. A *woman* in a scientific laboratory? Well, yes, the French had done that with Madame Curie after her husband had been killed in a traffic accident. In spite of this precedent, Fischer was reluctant. He compromised by telling Hahn that he could have Lise Meitner as an assistant if Miss Meitner promised not to enter a classroom or laboratory room where Fischer's male students were working. Lise Meitner worked with Hahn for thirty years. In 1911 they moved from the University laboratory to the newly founded Kaiser Wilhelm Institute for Chemistry. Since this was a research institution, women were not banned.

After a stretch of war service, Hahn in the German Army and Meitner as a nurse in the Austrian Army, they came together again in the Kaiser Wilhelm Institute and, in 1917, discovered element no. 91. Of course, it was radioactive and slowly turned into the long-known element actinium. For this reason they called it "before actinium," or "proto-actinium"; the name was later shortened to "protactinium."

At about the same time, Frederick Soddy and John A. Cranston in England discovered it, too. Because the First World War was still going on, communications were not good, but after the war it was established that Hahn and Meitner had been the first. In the meantime Hahn had gone over the work of other researchers and found that his protactinium was the same as the brevium that Fajans and Göhring had found in 1913. Hahn proposed to establish the older name, but the International Chemical Union would not hear of it. One could not call an element with a half-life of over 1,200 years "brevium." Fajans and Göhring, who happened to come across a short-lived isotope of protactinium, had been justified in their choice of name. But the new element of Hahn and Meitner was not short-lived and could not bear that name; protactinium it remained.

By 1923, when Coster and von Hevesy discovered hafnium, all the places in the Mendeleyeff table, as adapted by Moseley, had been filled except five. The missing elements were nos. 43, 61, 75, 85 and 87. Since all the elements with a higher atomic number than 83 (which is bismuth) are radioactive, it could be expected that nos. 85 and 87 would also be radioactive. The three others, it was reasoned, were not.

X. THE ATOMIC AGE

As had been assumed, element no. 75 was not radioactive and its detection was announced on September 5, 1925, during a meeting of the Society of German Chemists in Berlin. The president of the society said during his introduction of the speaker that this was a historic occasion for another reason, too. For the first time since the founding of the society, the speaker was a woman, namely, Dr. Ida Tacke. But while Lise Meitner had been requested to hide from Emil Fischer's male students in 1907, nobody was horrified, or even surprised, by the thought of a "scientific female" anymore.

Dr. Ida Tacke told the assembly that element no. 75 had been suspected to be in hiding in platinum-bearing ores and that she, in collaboration with Dr. Walter Noddack, had first tried to find it in such ores. That attempt had been unsuccessful, partly because the amount of ore had been quite small.

But they had found it after a long and tedious process of separation in gadolinite and had called it "rhenium," from *Rhenus,* the Latin name of the river Rhine. The first proof of the existence of this element had been obtained by spectrum analysis.

In the following years Drs. Noddack and Tacke became man and wife and they also produced a first and tiny sample of the pure metal. In 1928 they were supplied with 660 kilograms (1,450 lbs.) of molybdenum ores and extracted 1 gram of rhenium from the raw material.

After this difficult job had been performed, it was found that rhenium is more abundant in other ores, for example, in the South German copper-bearing slate first described by Agricola, and in molybdenite from Wisconsin.

During the next half dozen years several chemists thought that they had tracked down the other missing elements. Noddack and Tacke announced that they had also found element no. 43. They called it "masurium" in memory of the Battle of the Masurian Lakes in East Prussia in which Dr. Noddack had taken part as a twenty-one-year-old soldier. But it was a mistake; "masurium" was not found for years and exists in nature only if a uranium atom has recently been split by natural causes. The modern name of this element is "technetium" and the longest-lived isotope, the one of mass 95, has a half-life of only 60 days.

In 1926 Professor B. Smith Hopkins of the University of Illinois announced that he had found element no. 61 and named it "illinium"; its existence had been predicted by Mendeleyeff's friend, Professor Bohuslav Brauner (1855–1935) of the University in Prague. At about the same time, element no. 61 was also "discovered," by Professor Luigi Rolla of the University of Florence, who called it "florentium." The actual discovery did not take place until 1945 and it was then named "promethium." It is the only rare-earth element that does not have a single stable isotope. The longest-lived of the radioactive isotopes is the one of mass 147, with a half-life of about 2½ years.

Element no. 85, Mendeleyeff's eka-iodine, had been expected to be radioactive since its atomic number is larger than that of bismuth, but nobody expected it to be as short-lived as it actually is. When Drs. Fred Allison and Edgar J. Murphy of the Alabama Polytechnic Institute announced their "alabamine" in 1931, they probably expected it to be about as unstable as radium, but the longest-lived isotope of element no. 85, the one that has a mass of 210, has a half-life of just 8.3 hours! The announcement was a mistake, of course; the actual discovery did not take place until 1940 and it was named "astatine," from the Greek for "unsteady."

As for element no. 87, it had also been mistakenly announced by Allison and Murphy (in 1929) and had been named "virginium," for the native state of Dr. Allison. Ten years later a chemist named Horia Hulubey stated that he had finally found element no. 87 and proposed the name of "moldavium," after the river Moldau in Bohemia. Very soon after, still another woman in radiochemical research, Mademoiselle Marguerite Prey, in Paris, found proof that a certain unstable isotope with a mass of 223 and a half-life of 22 minutes had to be element no. 87. She proposed the now accepted name "francium." Astatine and francium are the two elements about which the least is known, even to this day.

The really important new discovery of that period was announced by Sir James Chadwick in 1932 and it did *not* concern a new element. It was something more fundamental. Up to that year only two subatomic particles had been assumed to exist—the negatively charged electron outside the nucleus and the positively charged proton (weighing about 1,840 times as much as an electron) in the nucleus. But there was a difficulty.

Helium had the atomic number 2, which meant that it carried two charges in the nucleus. But its atomic weight was 4, so it should have four protons in the nucleus and should, therefore, carry four electric charges. This could be explained only by assuming that two of the protons in the nucleus were electrically neutralized by the presence of two electrons in the nucleus (Figure 10). A helium atom, therefore, had to have four protons and two electrons in the nucleus, with two

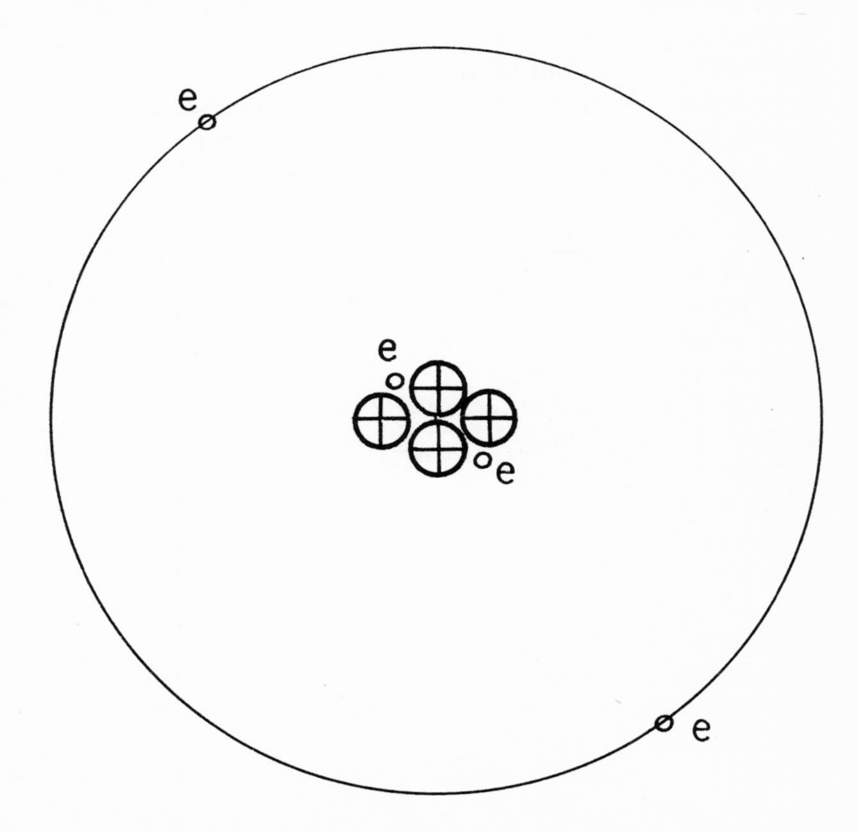

FIGURE 10. *Early concept of the helium atom, with two electrons in "orbit" and four protons plus two electrons in the nucleus.*

more electrons in orbit around it. This was still a reasonably simple picture, but if this explanation was true, then a uranium atom had to have 238 protons plus 146 electrons in the nucleus, with 92 electrons in orbit.

Sir James Chadwick had made experiments that had convinced him, and everybody else who learned about them, that there had to be another heavy particle like the proton. But this one did not carry an electric charge; it was electrically neutral and Chadwick called it a "neutron." Chemists and physicists interested in the structure of the atom sighed with relief; this got rid of the electrons in the nucleus. Now the helium atom had two protons and two neutrons in the nucleus, making the mass 4 with only two electric charges (Figure 11). Even the heavy uranium atom had grown a

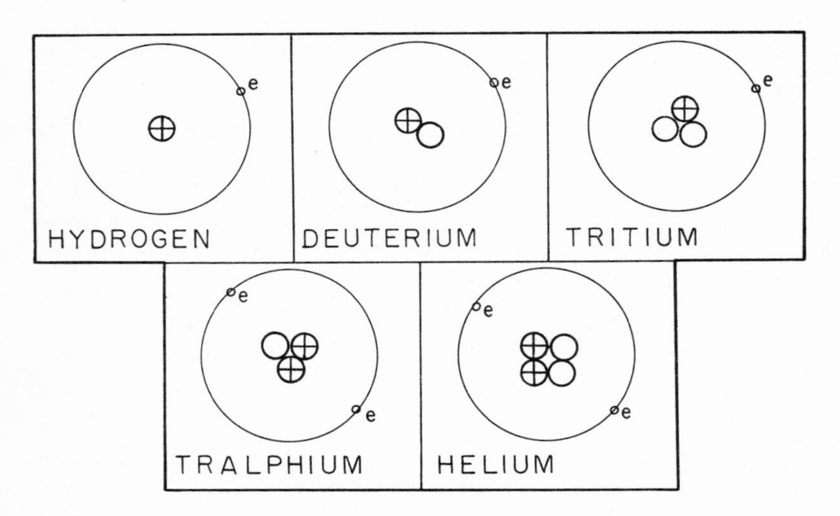

FIGURE 11. *The five lightest elements: ordinary hydrogen, "heavy hydrogen" or deuterium, hydrogen of mass = 3 or tritium, helium of mass = 3 or tralphium, and ordinary helium of mass = 4.*

little simpler: with 92 protons and 146 neutrons in the nucleus and 92 electrons in orbits in several layers. These layers came to be called "electron shells" or just "shells."

As if to prove Chadwick right as quickly as possible, a heavy isotope of hydrogen, named "deuterium," was discovered by the American researchers, Professors H. C. Urey, F. G. Brickwedde and G. M. Murphy. Its nucleus consisted of one proton and one neutron, producing mass 2 but with only one charge.

Then everybody realized with astonishment that old Prout had been right after all. If you called the particles in the nucleus—the protons and neutrons—"nucleons," then hydrogen had one (or two) nucleons, helium had four, lithium had six and seven, beryllium had nine, carbon had twelve and so on through the atomic table. The heavier elements were not clusters of hydrogen atoms, as Prout had said, but they could be called "clusters of hydrogen nuclei." Even those stubborn elements like chlorine that always showed an atomic weight of about 35.5 could be brought into line because of Soddy's discovery of isotopes. If one assumed that half of the atoms of chlorine had a mass of 35 and the other half belonged to an isotope with a mass of 36, the atomic weight had to come out as 35½ because the chemists had worked with the natural isotope mixture, not even knowing that there were isotopes.[1]

The next important discovery was made in France. During the year before she discovered radium, Madame Curie had had a baby, a daughter who was named Irène. Later Irène Curie (1897–1956) met an assistant of her mother by the name of Frédéric Joliot (1900–1958) and they were married.

[1] Actually the situation is a bit different: 75.53 percent of the chlorine atoms belong to the isotope with mass 35, while 24.47 percent belong to an isotope with mass 37, resulting in an average atomic weight of 35.457. These two isotopes, of course, differ only in the number of neutrons.

Joliot took the name Joliot-Curie, because the Curies had had no male children.

The Joliot-Curies almost became the discoverers of the neutron. Chadwick was the first only by a margin of a few months. Learning about his experiments, they realized that researchers had twice succeeded in changing the nucleus of an atom. Baron Rutherford, in 1919, had bombarded nitrogen with alpha particles (helium nuclei) and had obtained oxygen and hydrogen as a result. Then Chadwick had thrown helium nuclei at beryllium atoms and obtained carbon atoms, neutrons and gamma rays. The Joliot-Curies bombarded boron, aluminum, and magnesium with helium nuclei and found that radioactivity lingered for some time. They reasoned correctly that the atoms they had bombarded had become unstable and had continued to send out radiations until they had finally become stable atoms, but of another element.

This was the discovery of "artificial radioactivity," a concept that at first was completely misunderstood by most people.

Since the concept is still occasionally misunderstood, careful explanation is in order. The heavyweight elements, beginning with polonium, atomic number 84, are all *naturally* radioactive; they have no stable isotopes even though each one has quite a number of them. But some of the radioactive heavyweights have very long half-lives. For example, the uranium isotope of mass 238 has a half-life of 4,510,000,000 years. Among the lightweight elements there are just two, nos. 43 and 61, that are naturally radioactive and have no stable isotopes. All the other elements, from no. 1 (hydrogen) to no. 83 (bismuth) are stable and will not change naturally. But under alpha-particle or neutron bombardment—from naturally radioactive elements that happen to be close—some of the elements will form radioactive isotopes. They do not last long; an unstable isotope of a naturally stable element with a half-life of more than one year is a rarity.[2]

That unstable atoms of stable elements can occur in nature for a short period of time was not known when the Joliot-Curies produced such unstable atoms artificially. The aluminum atoms they had bombarded had become phosphorus atoms; the atoms had moved up in the atomic table by two places. But they were not stable phosphorus atoms, for they continued to change while giving off radiation. Naturally, the radiochemists, who nowadays are called nuclear physicists, were curious about what kinds of changes could take place.

Suppose you bombard an element with neutrons which have one unit of mass and no electric charge. The atom struck by the neutron may simply accept it. Since the neutron carries no charge, this does not change the atomic number of the element. Chemically it is still the same; it just has grown a bit heavier. If an atom of the element cadmium with a mass of 113 has been struck, it is now cadmium of the mass 114, which happens to be a stable isotope, too. But if an atom of silver with the mass 107 has been struck and has become an atom of silver with the mass of 108, we have produced an atom that is not stable. It has a half-life of only 2.3 minutes. It will eject an electron from its nucleus. The ejection of such an electron—since there are no electrons in the nucleus normally—means that an electron has been formed by the change of a neutron into a proton. Now this former neutron is a positively charged proton, and the atom has moved from no. 47 with a mass of 108 to no. 48 with a mass of 108. Element no. 48 is cadmium and cadmium of the mass 108 happens to be stable, so the process stops there. But if that particular

[2] The argon isotope of mass 39, with a half-life of 260 years, is one of these rare exceptions. The longest half-life of an unstable isotope of a naturally stable element is probably the isotope of krypton of the mass 81, with a half-life of 200,000 years.

isotope had been unstable, too, there would have been at least one more step.

If alpha particles are used for bombardment, the changes are greater, since the alpha particle has the mass 4 and carries two positive charges. If an atom of element no. 54 (xenon) with a mass of 131 (a stable isotope) absorbs an alpha particle, the atomic number jumps two places to no. 56, which is barium, and the weight jumps by four units to 135. The resulting atom then is barium of mass 135, often written as "barium-135," which happens to be stable.

On the other hand, if polonium that has the atomic number 84 shoots out an alpha particle, the resulting new atom must have the atomic number 82, which is lead. If the polonium atom had the mass 210, the new lead atom will have the mass 206, which is a stable lead isotope.

In order to write down such changes easily, nuclear physicists have developed a special method. The example just mentioned would be written as follows:

$${}_{84}Po^{210} - {}_{2}He^{4} \rightarrow {}_{82}Pb^{206}$$

meaning: element 84 (polonium) of mass 210 ejects element 2 (helium) of mass 4, resulting in element 82 (lead) of mass 206.

There are, of course, several other kinds of atomic reactions. However, the main thing to remember is that an element under either neutron or alpha-particle bombardment will move only two (in rare cases, three) places up or down in the atomic table, or only one place if the acceptance of a neutron should result in the change of a neutron into a proton. It can also go the other way, because a proton can change into a neutron; it does this by ejecting a particle called a "positron," which is positively charged but no larger than an electron. Nuclear physicists, if they obtained a new isotope, tried to establish its chemical nature by testing it for the chemical characteristics of the elements that are nearby in the Periodic Table.

Beginning in about 1933, the Italian physicist, Enrico Fermi (1901–1954) decided to investigate all of these subatomic reactions systematically by bombarding all available elements with neutrons. But when he bombarded uranium, he obtained not one new isotope, but several. It looked as if atoms heavier than uranium had resulted, as well as some lighter ones.

Figure 12 shows how the bottom row of the Periodic Table looked in 1933. Bombarded uranium might slide down two places and become thorium, and then might slide down two more places and become radium. Or else the uranium atoms might move up one, two, three or even four places and would then fill the empty spaces 93, 94, 95 and 96. Following Mendeleyeff's method, these new elements were tentatively called "eka-rhenium" for no. 93, "eka-osmium"' for no. 94, "eka-iridium" for no. 95 and "eka-platinum" for no. 96. The general name for them became "transuranic elements."

Otto Hahn and Lise Meitner in Berlin read about these experiments and decided to duplicate them; they were ably assisted by Dr. Fritz Strassmann, who had joined Otto Hahn at just about that time. Hahn bombarded uranium with neutrons and obtained results that were difficult to understand, but that seemed to confirm what Enrico Fermi had reported. Bombarded uranium produced several isotopes of radium and other isotopes that seemed to be transuranic elements, especially eka-osmium and eka-iridium. The only one who voiced doubts was Dr. Ida Noddack. In 1934 she wrote: "But one can also assume that the changes in the nucleus that have been brought about are of an entirely different kind. It is possible that the bombardment of these nuclei causes them to break apart into several large pieces which are isotopes of

37 Rb	38 Sr	39 Y	40 Zr	41 Nb	42 Mo	43 Tc	44 Ru	45 Rh	46 Pd
55 Cs	56 Ba	LA	72 Hf	73 Ta	74 W	75 Re	76 Os	77 Ir	78 Pt
87 Fr	88 Ra	AC	104	105	106	107	108	—	—

THE LANTHANIDES

La	Ce	Pr	Nd	Pm	Sm	Eu	Gd	Tb	Dy	Ho	Er	Tm	Yb	Lu
57	58	59	60	61	62	63	64	65	66	67	68	69	70	71

THE ACTINIDES

Ac	Th	Pa	U	Np	Pu	Am	Cm	Bk	Cf	E	Fm	Mv	No	Lw
89	90	91	92	93	94	95	96	97	98	99	100	101	102	103

FIGURE 12. *The bottom three rows of the atomic table as they actually look. Elements no. 89–103 were found to form a series similar to that of the rare-earth metals and with the same number of members. Hence the still undiscovered element no. 104 will resemble hafnium chemically, while no. 105 would resemble tantalum. Because the table shown in Fig. 8 was thought to be correct, the then undiscovered element no. 94 was assumed to resemble osmium, no. 95 was expected to resemble iridium, and no. 96 to resemble platinum.*

known elements, but not neighbors of the bombarded elements in the Periodic Table."

It happened that Ida Noddack was absolutely correct. The uranium atoms had broken up into isotopes of the elements barium (no. 56) and krypton (no. 36). But since no atoms had ever been broken up into roughly equal pieces before, Hahn, Meitner and Strassmann at first rejected the idea. They especially investigated the isotopes which they thought to be radium isotopes, but by 1939 Hahn and Strassmann (Lise Meitner had meanwhile left Germany and gone to Sweden) said that it was more likely that the so-called radium isotopes were barium isotopes. As the Periodic Table shows, radium is placed directly below barium, so these two elements are chemically similar. Only a few months after their first doubt that they were looking at radium isotopes, Hahn and Strassmann were certain.

The "fission" of uranium had been discovered.

And Lise Meitner produced mathematical proof that this fission was not the fission of uranium atoms generally, but only of the comparatively rare uranium isotope with mass 235.

Written in the same manner as the previous formula, the fission formula read:

$$_{92}U^{235} + {}_{0}n^{1} \rightarrow {}_{56}Ba^{\text{several}} + {}_{36}Kr^{\text{several}} + \text{several } {}_{0}n^{1}$$

and the most important item is that, in addition to several barium and several krypton isotopes, several free neutrons were formed, which could then hit other atoms, so the reaction is repeated over and over—in other words, a chain reaction is achieved.

This chain reaction finally led to the building of the first atomic bomb, but it also led to chemical research with entirely new means. What Fermi and Hahn had believed to be elements heavier than uranium were isotopes of the elements ruthenium, rhodium, palladium, silver, cadmium and indium. But true elements with masses greater than that of uranium were soon discovered. In 1940 Edwin M. Mcmillan and Philip H. Abelson, working at Berkeley, California, bombarded uranium-238 with neutrons. It first changed into uranium-239, then ejected an electron and became element no. 93. Since the planet Neptune is farther from the sun than the planet Uranus, they named element no. 93 "neptunium."

But neptunium is unstable; it ejects another electron and thereby becomes element no. 94, which was discovered in 1941 by Glenn T. Seaborg (later chairman of the Atomic Energy Commission), Emilio Segrè, and Ernest O. Lawrence.

Plutonium, since it will fission like uranium-235, became the second "atomic bomb element" and for this reason was produced in fairly large quantities. Unlike the silvery uranium, plutonium looks like lead. A certain plutonium isotope then gave element no. 95, americium, and the same team under Seaborg's direction gradually progressed to element no. 96, named "curium," no. 97, named "berkelium," and element no. 98, named "californium." Americium and curium were discovered, or rather made, in 1944, the others after the end of the Second World War.

In the Periodic Table element no. 93, neptunium, is below no. 75, rhenium, and element no. 94, plutonium, is below no. 76, osmium. Hence neptunium should resemble rhenium chemically and plutonium should resemble osmium. They don't. They resemble each other.

They also resemble uranium, protactinium and thorium. And their atomic weights do not differ very much. It was Glenn T. Seaborg who drew a conclusion from these facts: here we dealt with another "fraternal fifteen." The elements from no. 89 (actinium) to no. 103 (lawrencium) form a close-knit group like the rare-earth metals. Seaborg suggested that they be called the "actinides" and the Periodic Table was redrawn once more (Figure 12).

Therefore the true eka-rhenium, the one that should be in the table below rhenium and resemble it chemically, would be element no. 104.[3] And the true eka-osmium would be element no. 105.

[3] The making of a few atoms of element no. 104 was reported from the USSR in 1965, but not even its half-life is yet established.

They are still unknown. And, of course, they will be radioactive. But if either no. 104 or no. 105 should have an isotope with a half-life of a few days, or even only a few hours, so that its chemical characteristics can be investigated, we are likely to find that Mendeleyeff's table holds true even for the short-lived elements beyond the actinides.

APPENDIX I

ALPHABETICAL LIST OF THE NAMES OF THE ELEMENTS AND THEIR DERIVATIONS

ELEMENT	ATOMIC NUMBER	REMARKS
Actinium	89	from Greek *aktis,* "ray."
Aluminum	13	from *alumine,* or alum; "aluminium" in countries other than the U.S.
Americium	95	artificial element made in U.S.
Antimony	51	symbol (Sb) from Latin *stibium,* a mineral containing antimony. Origin of name is uncertain, possibly from *anti* (against) and *monium* ("isolated") because it combines readily. One German historian claims the

ELEMENT	ATOMIC NUMBER	REMARKS
		name comes from the opening words *anti monachon* ("against monks") of an edict criticizing excessive use of antimony compounds by monks for medicinal purposes. Decree *anti-monachon* by the French king, Francis II.
Argon	18	from the Greek for "lazy."
Arsenic	33	from the Greek name *arsenikon* for the trisulphide of arsenic, which was a much used yellow pigment.
Astatine	85	from Greek *astatos,* "unstable." (Name first proposed in 1931 was "alabamine.")
Barium	56	from Greek *barys,* "heavy."
Berkelium	97	artificial element made at Berkeley, Calif.
Beryllium	4	from the mineral beryl. Older name "glucinium" from the Greek word for "sweet," since solutions of its compounds have a sweetish taste. (The German word *Brille* for eye-glasses is derived from beryl, too; white beryls were tried for grinding into lenses.)
Bismuth	83	from the German *Wismut,* which is a corruption of *Weisse Masse* ("white mass") or of *Wiesematte* ("blossoming meadow") since the deposit in the furnace was white with colored spots, like flowers in a meadow.
Boron	5	from borax, its most common compound.
Bromine	35	from Greek *bromos,* "stench."

ELEMENT	ATOMIC NUMBER	REMARKS
Cadmium	48	from Latin *cadmia,* which really means "calamine"; cadmium often is found associated with it.
Calcium	20	from Latin *calcis,* "lime."
Californium	98	artificial element made at the University of California.
Carbon	6	from Latin *carbo,* "coal," more specifically "charcoal."
Cerium	58	discovered in 1803 and named after the minor planet, Ceres, which had been discovered two years earlier by Father Giuseppe Piazzi.
Cesium	55	from Latin *caesius* ("blue") after its blue lines in the spectrum.
Chlorine	17	from Greek *chloros,* meaning "light green," because of its color.
Chromium	24	from Greek *chroma,* "color," because it forms pigments.
Cobalt	27	from German *Kobold,* a mischievous mountain gnome who substituted "worthless" cobalt for the copper the miners wanted.
Copper	29	from Latin *cuprum,* the metal from Cyprus, pronounced "Keeprus" by the Greeks.
Curium	96	artificial element named in honor of Marie and Pierre Curie.
Dysprosium	66	from Greek *dysprositos,* "difficult to approach," or to find.
Einsteinium	99	artificial element named in honor of Albert Einstein.
Erbium	68	named after Ytterby, Sweden.
Europium	63	after Europe.
Fermium	100	artificial element named in honor of Enrico Fermi.

ELEMENT	ATOMIC NUMBER	REMARKS
Fluorine	9	from the mineral fluospar, used as a flux; hence the name, from Latin *fluo*, "flow."
Francium	87	after France. (Name first proposed in 1930 was "virginium.")
Gadolinium	64	named in honor of the Finnish chemist, Johan Gadolin.
Gallium	31	after France (Gallia).
Germanium	32	after Germany.
Gold	79	symbol (Au) from Latin name *aurum*, for "gold." The English name is probably derived from a Germanic root word meaning "yellow."
Hafnium	72	from Latin name (Hafnia) of Copenhagen.
Helium	2	from Greek sun god Helios, because it was first discovered in a spectrogram of sunlight.
Holmium	67	from the Latin name (Holmia) for Stockholm.
Hydrogen	1	from French *hydrogène*, "water maker."
Indium	49	from "indigo," the color of its lines in the spectrum; the indigo plant, of course, was named after India so this is a geographical name twice removed.
Iodine	53	from Greek *ion*, "violet."
Iridium	77	from Latin *iridis*, "rainbow"; the solutions of some of its compounds are iridescent.
Iron	26	symbol (Fe) from *ferrum*, the Latin name of this metal. Derivation of the English word is uncertain.
Krypton	36	from Greek *kryptos*, "hidden."

ELEMENT	ATOMIC NUMBER	REMARKS
Lanthanum	57	from Greek *lanthanei,* "to escape notice."
Lead	82	symbol (Pb) from Latin name *plumbum;* English word is related to "load"; Dutch name is *lood,* pronounced the same as "load." It is a heavy metal. The German name *Bleì* is related to "blue" because of the color of the fresh-cut metal; hence the often mistranslated German soldier's term, "blue beans" for bullets.
Lithium	3	from Greek *lithos,* "stone."
Lutetium	71	from the Latin name (Lutetia) of Paris. Formerly named Lutecium. (Auer von Welsbach proposed the name "cassiopeium," which was not accepted.)
Magnesium	12	after the district of Magnesia in ancient Greece.
Manganese	25	from Italian *manganese,* a corruption of the Latin word *magnesius,* which means "magnetic"—which manganese is not.
Mendelevium	101	artificial element named in honor of Dmitri Ivanovitch Mendeleyeff.
Mercury	80	symbol (Hg) from "hydrargyrum," a word compounded from Greek *hydor* ("water") and *argyros* ("silver"). The word "mercury" is the name of the fast-moving planet to to which it was assigned by the alchemists; the "quick" part of the alternate name "quicksilver" survives in the phrase "the quick and the dead."

ELEMENT	ATOMIC NUMBER	REMARKS
Molybdenum	42	from the Greek name *molybdos,* "lead"; the ore was believed to be lead ore.
Neodymium	60	from the Greek words *neos* ("new") and *didymos* ("twin"); neodymium and praseodymium turned out to be twins of "didymium" that had been thought to be a single element and had been so named because it was considered a "twin" of lanthanum.
Neon	10	from Greek *neos,* "new."
Neptunium	93	the first artificial element "beyond uranium," hence named after the planet Neptune, which is beyond Uranus.
Nickel	28	from German *Kupfernickel,* the "worthless" metal put into the mountain instead of copper by a *Nickelmann,* a (male) sprite of stagnant lakes and swamps.
Niobium	41	formerly "columbium" (because the ores had been found in America), named after Niobe, the daughter of Tantalus. (See: tantalum.)
Nitrogen	7	from French *nitrogène,* "maker of niter" (sodium or potassium nitrate).
Nobelium	102	artificial element named in honor of Alfred Nobel.
Osmium	76	from Greek *osme,* "smell" (noun).
Oxygen	8	from French *oxygène,* "maker of acids"—but oxygen-free acids are now known.
Palladium	46	named in 1803 after the minor planet Pallas, discovered in 1802 by Dr. Wilhelm Matthias Olbers.

ELEMENT	ATOMIC NUMBER	REMARKS
Phosphorus	15	from the Greek *phosphoros,* "bearer of light."
Platinum	78	from Spanish *platina,* "little silver"; the explorers would have preferred real silver.
Plutonium	94	the artificial element beyond neptunium; hence named for the planet Pluto, which is beyond Neptune.
Polonium	84	named by Mme. Sklodowska-Curie after her native country, Poland.
Potassium	19	from "potash"; symbol (K) is from *kalium,* derived from the Arabic *al kaljun,* meaning "wood-ash."
Praseodymium	59	from Greek *prasaios* ("leek green"; also the name of a green tree-frog) and *didymos,* "twin." Its salts are green. (See: neodymium.)
Promethium	61	from Prometheus. Name first proposed in 1926 was 'illinium" (from Illinois) but claims of discovery were not accepted.
Protactinium	91	shortened from original name "protoactinium"; first part of name from Greek *protos,* "first," because it decays into actinium.
Radium	88	from Latin *radius,* "ray."
Radon	86	originally called "niton" ("shining"), coined name using the name of radium with suffix "on" to indicate relationship with neon, argon, etc.
Rhenium	75	from the Latin name (Rhenus) of the Rhine.
Rhodium	45	from Greek *rhodon,* "rose"; has rose-colored salts.

ELEMENT	ATOMIC NUMBER	REMARKS
Rubidium	37	from Latin *rubidus,* "red"; produces red lines in the spectrum.
Ruthenium	44	from the Latin name (Ruthenia) of Russia.
Samarium	62	named after the Russian mining official, Col. Samarski.
Scandium	21	after Scandinavia.
Selenium	34	after the Greek word (*selene*) for the moon (because it is similar to tellurium, named for the earth).
Silicon	14	from Latin word (*silex*) for "flint," which is silicon dioxide.
Silver	47	symbol (Ag) from Latin *argentum;* derivation of English word unknown.
Sodium	11	from caustic soda; symbol (Na) from Latin *natrium.*
Strontium	38	named after an area in Scotland.
Sulphur	16	the Latin name of the substance.
Tantalum	73	named after Tantalus of Greek mythology, punished by being placed in water which receded when he tried to drink; the name was given either because of the difficulties encountered in isolating the element, or more likely, because tantalum forms few compounds.
Technetium	43	earlier name "masurium," after an area in East Prussia. Current name from Greek *techne,* "skill," or *technetos,* "skillful" in the meaning of "artificial."
Tellurium	52	from Latin name (Tellus) for the earth.
Terbium	65	from Ytterby, Sweden.
Thallium	81	from Greek *thallos,* "a young shoot,"

ELEMENT	ATOMIC NUMBER	REMARKS
		because of a bright green line in its spectrum.
Thorium	90	after the Norse god, Thor.
Thulium	69	after Thule, ancient name for northern Scandinavia.
Tin	50	symbol (Sn) from Latin name (*Stannum*) of the metal. Derivation of English name unknown.
Titanium	22	after the Titans of Greek mythology. It is *not* named after Titan, the largest moon of Saturn; the element was named in 1791; current names of Saturn's moons were suggested by Sir John Herschel in 1858.
Uranium	92	name given to commemorate the discovery of the planet Uranus in 1781 by Sir William Herschel.
Vanadium	23	after Vanadis, the Norse goddess of beauty and love.
Wolfram	74	from the mineral wolframite. Alternate name is "tungsten" (Swedish *tung sten,* meaning "heavy stone") but the metal was first obtained from wolframite and not from *tungstein,* or scheelite.
Xenon	54	from Greek *xenos,* "stranger."
Ytterbium	70	from Ytterby, Sweden. (Auer von Welsbach proposed the name "aldebaranium," which was not accepted.)
Zinc	30	from German *Zinke,* which, in this case, means "protrusion" or "protuberance," because the metal formed such protrusions in the furnace.
Zirconium	40	from its mineral, zircon.

APPENDIX II

ATOMIC TABLES BY FAMILIES OF ELEMENTS

The tables on the following pages give the atomic weight of the naturally occurring isotope mixture, the density compared to water, the melting point in degrees centigrade (boiling point in the case of gases, denoted by *), the stable isotopes and their relative abundance in the natural element and the number of known unstable isotopes. In the case of naturally radioactive elements that do not have a stable isotope, the half-life of the longest-lived isotope is given.

THE ALKALI METALS (IA FAMILY)

Atomic number	*Element*	*Chemical symbol*	*Atomic weight*	*Density*	*Melting point*	*Stable isotopes*	*Number of unstable isotopes*
3	Lithium	Li	6.940	1.84	1350	Li-6 (7.5%) Li-7 (92.5%)	3
11	Sodium (*Natrium*)	Na	22.997	0.93	97.5	Na-23 (100%)	5
19	Potassium (*Kalium*)	K	39.096	0.87	62.3	K-39 (93.08%) K-40 (0.0119%) K-41 (6.91%)	8
37	Rubidium	Rb	85.48	1.53	38.5	Rb-85 (72.2%) Rb-87 (27.8%)	20
55	Cesium	Cs	132.91	1.87	26.0	Cs-133 (100%)	21
87	Francium	Fr	—	—	—	none	8 (Fr-223 = 22 min.)

THE IB FAMILY

Atomic number	*Element*	*Chemical symbol*	*Atomic weight*	*Density*	*Melting point*	*Stable isotopes*	*Number of unstable isotopes*
29	Copper (*Cuprum*)	Cu	63.57	8.6	1083	Cu-63 (69%) Cu-65 (31%)	10
47	Silver (*Argentum*)	Ag	107.88	10.5	960.5	Ag-107 (51.4%) Ag-109 (48.6%)	23
79	Gold (*Aurum*)	Au	197.2	19.3	1063	Au-197 (100%)	20

THE ALKALINE EARTH METALS (IIA FAMILY)

Atomic number	*Element*	*Chemical symbol*	*Atomic weight*	*Density*	*Melting point*	*Stable isotopes*	*Number of unstable isotopes*
4	Beryllium	Be	9.02	1.84	1350	Be-9 (100%)	4
12	Magnesium	Mg	24.32	1.74	651	Mg-24 (78.8%)	3
						Mg-25 (10.1%)	
						Mg-26 (11.1%)	
20	Calcium	Ca	40.08	1.54	810	Ca-40 (96.9%)	6
						Ca-42 (0.64%)	
						Ca-43 (0.14%)	
						Ca-44 (2.1%)	
						Ca-46 (0.003%)	
						Ca-48 (0.18%)	
38	Strontium	Sr	87.63	2.55	800	Sr-84 (0.55%)	15
						Sr-86 (9.8%)	
						Sr-87 (7.0%)	
						Sr-88 (82.7%)	
56	Barium	Ba	137.36	3.78	850	Ba-130 (0.1%)	15
						Ba-132 (0.097%)	
						Ba-134 (2.42%)	
						Ba-135 (6.6%)	
						Ba-136 (7.8%)	
						Ba-137 (11.3%)	
						Ba-138 (71.7%)	
88	Radium	Ra	226.05	6.0	960	none	13 (Ra-226 = 1,620 years)

THE IIB FAMILY

Atomic number	Element	Chemical symbol	Atomic weight	Density	Melting point	Stable isotopes	Number of unstable isotopes
30	Zinc	Zn	65.38	7.1	419	Zn-64 (48.9%)	10
						Zn-66 (27.8%)	
						Zn-67 (4.1%)	
						Zn-68 (18.6%)	
						Zn-70 (0.63%)	
48	Cadmium	Cd	112.41	8.65	321	Cd-106 (1.22%)	13
						Cd-108 (0.88%)	
						Cd-110 (12.4%)	
						Cd-111 (12.8%)	
						Cd-112 (24.0%)	
						Cd-113 (12.3%)	
						Cd-114 (28.8%)	
						Cd-116 (7.6%)	
80	Mercury (*Hydrargium*)	Hg	200.61	13.6 (liquid)	−39	Hg-196 (0.15%)	17
						Hg-198 (10.1%)	
						Hg-199 (16.9%)	
						Hg-200 (23.1%)	
						Hg-201 (13.2%)	
						Hg-202 (29.8%)	
						Hg-204 (6.8%)	

The IIIA Family

Atomic number	Element	Chemical symbol	Atomic weight	Density	Melting point	Stable isotopes	Number of unstable isotopes
5	Boron	B	10.82	2.53	2300	B-10 (18.8%) B-11 (81.2%)	2
13	Aluminum	Al	26.97	2.7	660	Al-27 (100%)	6
31	Gallium	Ga	69.72	5.9	29.75	Ga-69 (60.1%) Ga-71 (39.9%)	10
49	Indium	In	114.76	7.28	155	In-113 (4.2%) In-115 (95.8%)	22
81	Thallium	Tl	204.39	11.86	303.5	Tl-203 (29.5%) Tl-205 (70.5%)	17

The IIIB Family *

Atomic number	Element	Chemical symbol	Atomic weight	Density	Melting point	Stable isotopes	Number of unstable isotopes
21	Scandium	Sc	45.10	3.62	1200	Sc-45 (100%)	12
39	Yttrium	Y	88.92	3.80	1490	Y-89 (100%)	17

* NOTE: *The Lanthanides and the Actinides in this family are listed separately.*

The IVA Family

Atomic number	Element	Chemical symbol	Atomic weight	Density	Melting point	Stable isotopes	Number of unstable isotopes
6	Carbon	C	12.011	2.25	ca 3500	C-12 (98.89%)	4
						C-13 (1.11%)	
14	Silicon	Si	28.09	2.4	1420	Si-28 (92.17%)	4
						Si-29 (4.71%)	
						Si-30 (3.12%)	
32	Germanium	Ge	72.60	5.46	958.5	Ge-70 (20.5%)	11
						Ge-72 (27.4%)	
						Ge-73 (7.8%)	
						Ge-74 (36.5%)	
						Ge-76 (7.8%)	
50	Tin (*Stannum*)	Sn	118.70	7.29	231.8	Sn-112 (1.02%)	19
						Sn-114 (0.69%)	
						Sn-115 (0.38%)	
						Sn-116 (14.3%)	
						Sn-117 (7.6%)	
						Sn-118 (24.1%)	
						Sn-119 (8.5%)	
						Sn-120 (32.5%)	
						Sn-122 (4.8%)	
						Sn-124 (6.1%)	
82	Lead (*Plumbum*)	Pb	207.21	11.34	327.5	Pb-204 (1.3%)	21
						Pb-206 (26.0%)	
						Pb-207 (20.7%)	
						Pb-208 (52%)	

THE IVB FAMILY

Atomic number	Element	Chemical symbol	Atomic weight	Density	Melting point	Stable isotopes	Number of unstable isotopes
22	Titanium	Ti	47.90	4.5	1800	Ti-46 (8.00%)	4
						Ti-47 (7.4%)	
						Ti-48 (73.8%)	
						Ti-49 (5.5%)	
						Ti-50 (5.3%)	
40	Zirconium	Zr	91.22	6.44	1700	Zr-90 (51.5%)	10
						Zr-91 (11.2%)	
						Zr-92 (17.1%)	
						Zr-96 (2.8%)	
72	Hafnium	Hf	178.6	13.3	1700	Hf-174 (0.18%)	10
						Hf-176 (5.2%)	
						Hf-177 (18.5%)	
						Hf-178 (21.1%)	
						Hf-179 (13.8%)	
						Hf-180 (35.2%)	

THE VA FAMILY

Atomic number	Element	Chemical symbol	Atomic weight	Density	Melting point	Stable isotopes	Number of unstable isotopes
7	Nitrogen	N	14.008	0.81 (liquid)	−195·3*	N-14 (99.63%) N-14 (0.37%)	4
15	Phosphorus	P	30.98	1.83 (white P.)	44.1	P-31 (100%)	6
33	Arsenic	As	74·91	5·73	814	As-75 (100%)	12
51	Antimony (*Stibium*)	Sb	121.76	6.62	630.5	Sb-121 (57%) Sb-123 (43%)	27
83	Bismuth	Bi	209.00	9.80	271	Bi-209 (100%)	20

THE VB FAMILY

Atomic number	Element	Chemical symbol	Atomic weight	Density	Melting point	Stable isotopes	Number of unstable isotopes
23	Vanadium	V	50.95	5.69	1710	V-50 (0.25%) V-51 (99.75%)	7
41	Niobium	Nb	92.91	8.4	1950	Nb-93 (100%)	19
73	Tantalum	Ta	180.88	16.6	2850	Ta-180 (0.012%) Ta-181 (99.988%)	13

THE VIA FAMILY

Atomic number	*Element*	*Chemical symbol*	*Atomic weight*	*Density*	*Melting point*	*Stable isotopes*	*Number of unstable isotopes*
8	Oxygen	O	16.00	1.14 (liquid)	−183.0*	O-16 (99.759%) O-17 (0.037%) O-18 (0.204%)	3
16	Sulphur	S	32.06	2.0	112.8	S-32 (95.0%) S-33 (0.75%) S-34 (4.2%) S-36 (0.017%)	4
34	Selenium	Se	78.96	4.5	688	Se-74 (0.93%) Se-76 (9.1%) Se-77 (7.5%) Se-78 (23.6%) Se-80 (49.9%) Se-82 (9.0%)	16
52	Tellurium	Te	127.61	6.25	452	Te-120 (0.091%) Te-122 (2.5%) Te-123 (0.88%) Te-124 (4.6%) Te-125 (7.0%) Te-126 (18.7%) Te-128 (31.8%) Te-130 (34.4%)	18
84	Polonium	Po	—	—	—	none	24 (Po-209 = 103 years)

The VIB Family

Atomic number	Element	Chemical symbol	Atomic weight	Density	Melting point	Stable isotopes	Number of unstable isotopes
24	Chromium	Cr	52.01	6.92	1615	Cr-50 (4.41%)	6
						Cr-52 (83.76%)	
						Cr-53 (9.55%)	
						Cr-54 (2.38%)	
42	Molybdenum	Mo	95.95	9.01	2620	Mo-92 (15.9%)	9
						Mo-94 (9.1%)	
						Mo-95 (15.7%)	
						Mo-96 (16.5%)	
						Mo-97 (9.5%)	
						Mo-98 (23.8%)	
						Mo-100 (9.5%)	
74	Wolfram	W	183.92	19.0	3370	W-180 (0.14%)	12
						W-182 (26.2%)	
						W-183 (14.3%)	
						W-184 (30.7%)	
						W-186 (28.7%)	

THE HALOGENS (VIIA FAMILY)

Atomic number	*Element*	*Chemical symbol*	*Atomic weight*	*Density*	*Melting point*	*Stable isotopes*	*Number of unstable isotopes*
9	Fluorine	F	19.00	1.14 (liquid)	−187*	F-19 (100%)	4
17	Chlorine	Cl	35.457	1.507 (liquid)	−34.6*	Cl-35 (75.53%) Cl-37 (24.47%)	9
35	Bromine	Br	79.91	3.12 (liquid)	58.78*	Br-79 (50.6%) Br-81 (49.4%)	17
53	Iodine	I	126.92	4.94	113.5	I-127 (100%)	20
85	Astatine	At	—	—	470	none	20 (At-210 = 8.3 h.)

THE VIIB FAMILY

Atomic number	*Element*	*Chemical symbol*	*Atomic weight*	*Density*	*Melting point*	*Stable isotopes*	*Number of unstable isotopes*
25	Manganese	Mn	54.94	7.42	1260	Mn-55 (100%)	9
43	Technetium	Tc	—	11.5	ca. 2300	none	21 (Tc-97 = 2.6 mill. y.)
75	Rhenium	Re	186.22	20.5	ca. 3000	Re-185 (37.1%) Re-187 (62.9%)	17

THE NOBLE GASES (VIIIA FAMILY)

Atomic number	*Element*	*Chemical symbol*	*Atomic weight*	*Density (liquid)*	*Boiling point*	*Stable isotopes*	*Number of unstable isotopes*
2	Helium	He	4.003	0.15	−268.9	He-4 (100%)	3
10	Neon	Ne	20.183	0.90	−245.9	Ne-20 (90.92%)	4
						Ne-21 (0.26%)	
						Ne-22 (8.82%)	
18	Argon	A	39.944	1.42	−185.7	A-36 (0.337%)	5
						A-38 (0.063%)	
						A-40 (99.60%)	
36	Krypton	Kr	83.7	2.16	−151.8	Kr-78 (0.35%)	19
						Kr-80 (2.25%)	
						Kr-82 (11.60%)	
						Kr-83 (11.50%)	
						Kr-84 (57.00%)	
						Kr-86 (17.30%)	
54	Xenon	Xe	131.3	3.52	−109.1	Xe-124 (0.094%)	21
						Xe-126 (0.092%)	
						Xe-129 (26.4%)	
						Xe-130 (4.1%)	
						Xe-131 (21.2%)	
						Xe-132 (26.9%)	
						Xe-134 (10.4%)	
						Xe-136 (8.9%)	
86	Radon	Rn	222	9.74	−61.8	none	16 (Ra-222 = 3.825 days)

The VIIIB Family

Atomic number	*Element*	*Chemical symbol*	*Atomic weight*	*Density*	*Melting point*	*Stable isotopes*	*Number of unstable isotopes*
26	Iron					Fe-54 (5.87%)	6
	(*Ferrum*)	Fe	55.85	7.85	1535	Fe-56 (91.6%)	
						Fe-57 (2.2%)	
						Fe-58 (0.33%)	
27	Cobalt	Co	58.94	8.9	1480	Co-59 (100%)	11
28	Nickel	Ni	58.71	8.7	1452	Ni-58 (68.0%)	6
						Ni-60 (26.2%)	
						Ni-61 (1.1%)	
						Ni-62 (3.7%)	
						Ni-64 (1.2%)	
44	Ruthenium	Ru	101.1	12.06	2450	Ru-96 (5.6%)	9
						Ru-98 (1.9%)	
						Ru-99 (12.7%)	
						Ru-100 (12.7%)	
						Ru-101 (17.0%)	
						Ru-102 (31.5%)	
						Ru-104 (18.6%)	
45	Rhodium	Rh	102.91	12.44	1955	Rh-103 (100%)	18
46	Palladium	Pd	106.4	12.16	1555	Pd-102 (1.0%)	15

THE VIIIB FAMILY (*continued*)

Atomic number	*Element*	*Chemical symbol*	*Atomic weight*	*Density*	*Melting point*	*Stable isotopes*	*Number of unstable isotopes*
						Pd-104 (11.0%)	
						Pd-105 (22.2%)	
						Pd-106 (27.3%)	
						Pd-108 (26.7%)	
						Pd-110 (11.8%)	
76	Osmium	Os	190.2	22.5	2700	Os-184 (0.018%)	13
						OS-186 (1.59%)	
						Os-187 (1.64%)	
						Os-188 (13.3%)	
						Os-189 (16.1%)	
						Os-190 (26.4%)	
						Os-192 (41.0%)	
77	Iridium	Ir	192.2	22.42	2350	Ir-191 (38.5%)	16
						Ir-193 (61.5%)	
78	Platinum	Pt	195.09	21.37	1755	Pt-190 (0.012%)	11
						Pt-192 (0.78%)	
						Pt-194 (32.8%)	
						Pt-195 (33.7%)	
						Pt-196 (25.4%)	
						Pt-198 (7.2%)	

THE LANTHANIDES (ELEMENTS NOS. 57–71)

Atomic number	*Element*	*Chemical symbol*	*Atomic weight*	*Density*	*Melting point*	*Stable isotopes*	*Number of unstable isotopes*
57	Lanthanum	La	138.92	6.5	826	La-139 (100%)	14
58	Cerium	Ce	140.13	6.9	770	Ce-136 (0.19%)	12
						Ce-138 (0.26%)	
						Ce-140 (88.47%)	
						Ce-142 (11.08%)	
59	Praseodymium	Pr	140.92	6.47	940	Pr-141 (100%)	11
60	Neodymium	Nd	144.27	6.96	840	Nd-142 (27.1%)	7
						Nd-143 (12.2%)	
						Nd-144 (23.9%)	
						Nd-145 (8.3%)	
						Nd-146 (17.2%)	
						Nd-148 (5.7%)	
						Nd-150 (5.6%)	
61	Promethium	Pm	—	—	—	none	13 (Pm-145 = 18 y.)
62	Samarium	Sm	150.35	7.7	1350	Sm-144 (3.1%)	8
						Sm-147 (15.0%)	
						Sm-148 (11.2%)	
						Sm-149 (13.8%)	
						Sm-150 (7.4%)	

THE LANTHANIDES (*continued*)

Atomic number	*Element*	*Chemical symbol*	*Atomic weight*	*Density*	*Melting point*	*Stable isotopes*	*Number of unstable isotopes*
						Sm-152 (26.8%)	
						Sm-154 (28.7%)	
63	Europium	Eu	152.0	5.24	1100	Eu-151 (47.8%)	15
						Eu-153 (52.5%)	
64	Gadolinium	Gd	157.26	7.95	1350	Gd-152 (0.20%)	8
						Gd-154 (2.15%)	
						Gd-155 (14.70%)	
						Gd-156 (20.50%)	
						Gd-157 (15.70%)	
						Gd-158 (24.90%)	
						Gd-160 (21.90%)	
65	Terbium	Tb	158.93	8.33	1400	Tb-159 (100%)	13
66	Dysprosium	Dy	162.51	8.56	1475	Dy-156 (0.05%)	12
						Dy-158 (0.09%)	
						Dy-160 (2.29%)	
						Dy-161 (18.90%)	
						Dy-162 (25.50%)	
						Dy-163 (25.0%)	
						Dy-164 (28.2%)	
67	Holmium	Ho	164.94	8.76	1475	Ho-165 (100%)	12

THE LANTHANIDES (*continued*)

Atomic number	*Element*	*Chemical symbol*	*Atomic weight*	*Density*	*Melting point*	*Stable isotopes*	*Number of unstable isotopes*
68	Erbium	Er	167.27	9.06	1475	Er-162 (0.136%)	8
						Er-164 (1.54%)	
						Er-166 (33.40%)	
						Er-167 (22.90%)	
						Er-168 (27.10%)	
						Er-170 (14.90%)	
69	Thulium	Tm	168.94	9.34	1500	Tm-169 (100%)	7
70	Ytterbium	Yb	173.04	9.01	824	Yb-168 (0.14%)	7
						Yb-170 (3.03%)	
						Yb-171 (14.3%)	
						Yb-172 (21.8%)	
						Yb-173 (16.2%)	
						Yb-174 (31.8%)	
						Yb-176 (12.7%)	
71	Lutetium	Lu	174.99	9.74	1650	Lu-175 (97.4%)	12
						Lu-176 (2.6%)	

THE ACTINIDES (NO STABLE ISOTOPES)

Atomic number	*Element*	*Chemical symbol*	*Atomic weight*	*Density*	*Number of known isotopes and longest half-life*
89	Actinium	Ac	—	—	10; Ac-227 (22 y.)
90	Thorium	Th	232.05	11.13	15; Th-232 (13,900 million y.)
91	Protactinium	Pa	—	—	13; Pa-231 (34,000 y.)
92	Uranium	U	238.07	18.7	15; U-238 (4500 million y.)
93	Neptunium	Np	?	17.7	12; Np-236 (5000 + y.)
94	Plutonium	Pu	?	ca. 18.0	16; Pu-239 (24,300 y.)
95	Americium	Am	—	—	11; Am-243 (ca. 8000 y.)
96	Curium	Cm	—	—	13; Cm-245 (11,000 y.)
97	Berkelium	Bk	—	—	8; Bl-247 (7000 y.)
98	Californium	Cf	—	—	11; Cf-251 (ca. 800 y.)
99	Einsteinium	E	—	—	11; E-252 (ca. 150 d.)
100	Fermium	Fm	—	—	7; Fm-252 (30 h.)
101	Mendelevium	Mv	—	—	Mv-256 (ca ½ h.)
102	Nobelium	No	—	—	No-254 (3 sec.)
103	Lawrencium	Lw	—	—	Lw-257 (?)

APPENDIX III

BIBLIOGRAPHY

(NOTE: *College textbooks on inorganic chemistry and articles in scientific periodicals are not listed in this bibliography. Some important articles in periodicals have been mentioned in the text or in footnotes.*)

BUGGE, GÜNTHER. *Das Buch der grossen Chemiker.* Berlin: Verlag Chemie, 1929. Vol. I. 496 pp., 62 illustrations.
The book, written by no less than 23 historians of science, contains a total of 38 great chemists; the earliest entry is Zosimos of Egypt (*ca.* 400 B.C.), the latest, the German Schönbein (1799–1868). Only this first volume of the work appeared, though the original plan foresaw two volumes with a supplement to be published at a later date.

CONANT, JAMES BRYANT. *Robert Boyle's Experiments in Pneumatics.* Cambridge: Harvard University Press, 1955. 70 pp., diagrams.

This is #1 of the *Harvard Case Histories in Experimental Science,* prepared by Harvard University for students who are *not* science majors.

———. *The Overthrow of the Phlogiston Theory.* Cambridge: Harvard University Press, 1950. 59 pp. 3 illustrations.

This is #2 of the *Harvard Case Histories.*

CURIE, EVE. *Madame Curie, a Biography.* Garden City, N.Y.: Doubleday, 1938. 412 pp. photographs.

A biography of the discoverer of polonium and co-discoverer of radium by her daughter, Eve.

DALTON, JOHN. *A New System of Chemical Philosophy.* London: William Dawson & Sons, Ltd., 1964, 2 vols. 559 + 357 pp.

A facsimile reproduction of John Dalton's famous work which reintroduced the concept of atoms to chemistry. Volume I originally appeared in 1808, volume II in 1827.

FRIEND, J. NEWTON. *Man and the Chemical Elements.* London: Charles Griffin & Co., Ltd., 1951. 354 pp., illustrated.

A good account of the discovery of the elements and their uses, especially the early uses. Somewhat out of date by now.

GRAUBARD, MARK. *Astrology and Alchemy, Two Fossil Sciences.* New York: Philosophical Library, 1953. 382 pp., diagrams.

A popular work treating the two disciplines mentioned in the title as sciences of their times.

HAHN, OTTO. *Vom Radiothor zur Uranspaltung; Eine wissenschaftliche Selbstbiographie.* Braunschweig: Friedrich Vieweg & Sohn, 1962. 156 + 48 pp. with many photographs.

The "scientific autobiography" of the discoverer of uranium fission. An English edition, translated by Willy Ley and with an Introduction by Glenn T. Seaborg, was published by Charles Scribner's Sons in 1966.

HAMPEL, CLIFFORD A. (editor). *Rare Metals Handbook.* New York: Reinhold Publishing Corp., 1954. 657 pp., illustrated.

Treating all the rare metals, including the rare-earth metals, their ores, production and uses, with the greatest of detail. (This is a technical work, not for beginners.)

NASH, LEONARD K. *The Atomic-Molecular Theory*. Cambridge: Harvard University Press, 1950. 115 pp., no illustrations.
This is #4 of the *Harvard Case Histories*.

PILGRIM, E. *Entdeckung der Elemente*. Stuttgart: Mundus Verlag, 1950. 432 pp., with many photographs.
A rather valuable work, thorough and reliable and not written for chemists only, that has unfortunately never been translated.

POSIN, DANIEL Q. *Mendeleyev; The Story of a Great Scientist*. New York: Whittlesey House, 1948. 345 pp., photographs.
A thorough and very readable biography of the Russian chemist who was one of the most important innovators in his science.

ROLLER, DUANE. *The Early Development of the Concepts of Temperature and Heat*. Cambridge: Harvard University Press, 1950. 106 pp. illustrated.
This is #3 of the *Harvard Case Histories*.

SEABORG, GLENN T. *The Transuranium Elements*. New Haven: Yale University Press, 1958. 328 p., with many diagrams.
Originally four Silliman Lectures delivered at Yale University by Dr. Glenn T. Seaborg in May 1957. Dr. Seaborg is responsible for the discovery of several of these elements. (This is a professional work, not for beginners.)

———, and VALENS, EVANS G. *Elements*. New York: E. P. Dutton & Co., 1958. 253 pp., with many photographs and diagrams.
Probably realizing that a wider public should be informed about his work, Dr. Seaborg, after publishing the preceding volume, wrote this book, which ranges over the whole table of elements. This one *is* for the beginner.

STILLMAN, JOHN MAXSON. *The Story of Alchemy and Early Chemistry*. New York: Dover Publications, 1950. 566 pp., no illustrations.
Appeared originally in 1924 under the title *The Story of Early Chemistry;* the Dover reprint, listed here, is unabridged and unchanged.

TAYLOR, F. SHERWOOD. *The Alchemists, Founders of Modern Chemistry*. New York: Henry Schuman, 1949. 246 pp., with many illustrations.

A well-written account of the period when philosophers tried to be chemists, or the other way around, and enthusiastically failed in both disciplines.

VACZEK, LOUIS. *The Enjoyment of Chemistry.* New York: The Viking Press, 1964. 243 pp., no illustrations.
A popular book designed to acquaint the public with the thought processes of chemists and the rules of chemical behavior.

WEEKS, MARY ELVIRA. *Discovery of the Elements.* Published by the *Journal of Chemical Education,* New York, first edition 1939. 470 pages, with many illustrations.
A very valuable book that has been reissued and revised repeatedly.

INDEX